PLANTS OF THE
GALÁPAGOS ISLANDS

PLANTS OF THE GALÁPAGOS ISLANDS

Eileen K. Schofield
Illustrated by the author

UNIVERSE BOOKS
New York

To my fellow Galápagos travelers, whose enthusiasm inspired me to write this book.

Front cover: Spectacular view of volcanic scenery from the top of Bartolomé.
Back cover: On South Plaza, tree cactus (*Opuntia*) grows with the red herb *Sesuvium*, and the rocks are covered with lichens.

Published in the United States of America in 1984
by Universe Books
381 Park Avenue South, New York, N.Y. 10016

84 85 86 87 88 / 10 9 8 7 6 5 4 3 2 1

Printed in the United States of America

Library of Congress Cataloging in Publication Data

Schofield, Eileen K., 1939–
    Plants of the Galapagos Islands.

    Includes index.
    1. Botany—Galapagos Islands. 2. Plants—Identification. 3. Galapagos Islands—Description and travel—Guide-books. I. Title.
QK473.G2S36 1984   582.09866′5   83-40562
ISBN 0-87663-414-5

CONTENTS

INTRODUCTION

The Galápagos Islands (Archipiélago de Colón) are located in the Pacific Ocean, approximately 600 miles west of Ecuador. They were discovered in 1535 by the Bishop of Panama whose ship was blown off course while sailing to Peru, and they were named after the Spanish word for the large land tortoises found there. In the 1700s and 1800s, the islands became a regular stop for explorers, buccaneers, and whaling ships. The attractions were fresh water and tortoise meat. During that time the introduction of alien plants and animals and the decimation of native animals began.

The botanical history started with the first plant collections, made in 1825 by naturalists on two separate expeditions. James Macrae visited only Isabela; David Douglas and John Scouler collected mainly on Santiago, but many of their specimens were lost on the voyage home. The most famous early visitor to the Galápagos was Charles Darwin, who spent a month there in 1835. He collected plants on four islands and was able to reach the wet forest zone on two of them. His observations of the variations in plant and animal species on different islands were crucial in the development of his theory of evolution.

Darwin's major plant collection and several smaller sets found their way to Sir Joseph Hooker at Kew Gardens in England. He used them to compile the first flora of the Galápagos Islands in 1847, listing 236 ferns and flowering plants.

In the following years, several scientific expeditions visited the islands, and some made significant contributions to botany. The California Academy of Sciences sent Alban Stewart, who managed to collect plants on nearly every island. His studies resulted in a book listing more than 600 species. In 1932 members of the Templeton Crocker Expedition climbed almost to the top of Santa Cruz and were the first to see all the vegetation zones.

More recently, individual scientists have observed various aspects of Galápagos biology. The tortoises and several groups of birds have been studied in depth. Fossil pollen grains have revealed the past history of the climate and vegetation. Botanists have concentrated on the ecology of plant communities and conservation of the vegetation. In 1971 a cooperative effort produced the latest flora for the islands, describing about 700 ferns and flowering plants. Over a third of these are endemic, growing only in the Galápagos. Since then, a number of new species have been added and a list of 500 mosses, liverworts, and lichens has been compiled.

This variety of plants is able to grow on the small islands (total land area about 3,000 square miles) because of the favorable climate. From December to June the average high temperature is 85°F, and there are intermittent rains, most likely in January and February. From July to November, temperatures are cooler (high around 70°) and it is dry. Often there is a mist or cloud cover at higher elevations. In all months the equatorial sun is very hot, raising temperatures on sand or lava flows.

The islands are entirely volcanic and composed of lava, some fresh and some decomposed into soil, or sand to form beaches. Eastern islands are the oldest (3 million years), while the western Isabela and Fernandina are younger and still active volcanically. On Santiago there are lava flows dating from the early 1900s that are just starting to be colonized by plants.

The vegetation can be divided into six zones, most of them correlated to development of soil from lava to dry sand to rich organic soil. The zones blend naturally into each other, but are best observed on Santa Cruz, going from the shore to the island's summit.

1. The Littoral Zone includes the stands of several kinds of mangrove trees along the coast and the plants of sand dunes.

2. The Dry Zone is dominated by unique cactus shrubs or trees. There are also many small, succulent species and other shrubs. On smaller islands of low elevation this is the only vegetation that can flourish.

3. The cactus forest gradually changes into the Transition Zone. Many kinds of trees, shrubs, and herbs grow here, but the most characteristic is the silvery-gray *Bursera* tree.

4. The mixed forest gives way to the Scalesia Zone, named for the dominant tree, another unique Galápagos plant. Beneath the canopy of trees are vines, shrubs, orchids, bromeliads, and ferns. The effect is similar to wet tropical forest, completely different from the desert below.

5. Next comes the Miconia Zone, also named for its chief plant, a shrub that grows only in Galápagos. Beneath the shrubs are many ferns, some herbs, and club mosses.

6. At the top of the higher islands is the Fern-Sedge Zone, a low-growing vegetation with grasses, sedges, herbs, and ferns. Standing out are clusters of the Galápagos tree fern.

These upper zones are maintained by the fog and cloud cover that hangs over the islands above 3,000 feet. Because of the nearly constant supply of water, the plants there remain lush and green. In the dry zones, plants have had to develop ways of coping with the lack of fresh water for several months each year.

Some can grow in salt water (mangroves) or obtain water from salt spray (lichens). Some have succulent stems (cactus) or leaves (*Sesuvium*) that store water. Others are covered with tiny hairs that reflect sun and help keep in moisture (*Tiquilia*). Trees like *Bursera* live most of the year in a dormant condition, but come to life in the brief rainy season. They put out leaves, flowers, and fruits, disperse their seeds, and return to dormancy again. However, other species bloom at nearly any time of year.

Since the Galápagos always have been separated from the mainland, all of the plants living there must have arrived via long-distance dispersal. Most of them were derived from South America, but some seem to be related to species of Mexico or Central America. Evidence shows that birds have been the major vector of dispersal, carrying seeds internally or attached to their feathers. A second source has been wind, blowing in tiny spores and seeds with tufts of hairs that help them stay aloft. Other fruits have floated across the ocean, mostly mangroves and other shore species. In modern times, humans have become the new source of plants, often introducing unwelcome weeds.

Most native Galápagos plants have white or yellow flowers. Flower color is linked closely to type of pollination. Yellow flowers usually can be <u>pollinated by a variety of</u> insects (or birds), while <u>red flowers often are more</u> specialized. Since pollinators are not plentiful on islands, plants that are more generalized have a better chance of survival.

Some of the Galápagos birds and reptiles have close relationships, other than pollination, with the native plants. Tortoises eat many species and are beneficial to at least one. Seeds of the Galápagos tomato germinate best after passing through the intestinal tract of a tortoise. Marine iguanas dine on seaweeds, and land iguanas enjoy plants of the dry zone. They seem to be attracted to the yellow flowers of *Opuntia* and *Portulaca*, but at other seasons readily eat leaves and even spiny cactus pads. Darwin's finches eat and help disperse the seeds of *Croton*.

This carefully balanced ecosystem can be damaged easily by disturbance or by the introduction of alien plants and animals. Human visitors and inhabitants have left behind an assortment of animals that prey on native species. The worst threat to vegetation is the goat. It is estimated that there may be 100,000 goats on Santiago! Areas of vegetation are being protected by fences until a way can be found to eliminate these animals. Smaller islands already have been cleared of goats, and the vegetation has returned, sprouting from seeds and rootstocks hidden in the ground.

Cattle grazing has greatly reduced the Miconia Zone. In fact, the zone has been nearly destroyed on San Cristobal and is in danger on Santa Cruz. When an area is disturbed by grazing, there is the additional threat that introduced plants will move in and take over.

In the Galápagos there are more than 150 plants introduced by humans—everything from roses to balsa trees. Many are grown in gardens and cause no trouble. Others were meant to be commercial crops, but when experiments failed, the settlers went elsewhere, leaving the trees behind. The rich soil of the Scalesia Zone is the best for agriculture, so planted trees like avocado, quinine, and tropical guava are invading this native forest.

Interest in Galápagos conservation started in the 1950s. By 1959 the Charles Darwin Foundation was inaugurated, and all uninhabited land of the islands was declared a national park.

In 1964 the research station on Santa Cruz opened. Recently, the islands were named a province of Ecuador and one of the few natural areas on the World Heritage list.

The primary concern of the research station was saving the giant tortoise. Rearing young tortoises at the station, safe from predatory introduced animals, has helped stabilize the remaining population. A recent crisis brought about a similar program to rescue land iguanas. Plants have not been neglected, and work continues to eliminate goats and introduced trees.

In addition to maintaining these important projects, the national park personnel now must deal with approximately 14,000 tourists each year. Trained guides accompany all groups along trails that have been marked on each island. So far there has been little noticeable damage to the ecosystem, but further development should be controlled. With the continued cooperation and support of tourists and scientists, the future of the Galápagos looks promising.

As visitors to the Galápagos, you will enjoy a unique experience, seeing at close range the tame animals and birds in a setting of stark volcanic landscapes. It is hoped that this book will help you to appreciate better the unusual plants that are such an important part of the Galápagos ecosystem.

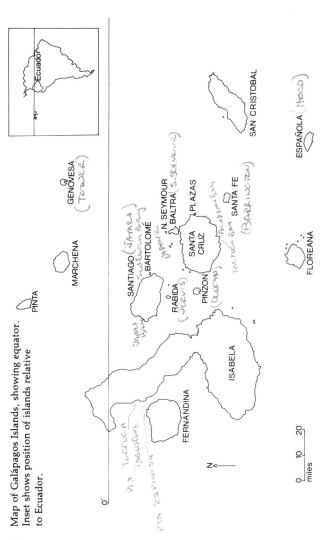

Map of Galápagos Islands, showing equator.
Inset shows position of islands relative
to Ecuador.

11

ISLANDS AND LOCALITIES

Over the centuries, the islands of the Galápagos group have received several sets of names. Since Ecuador became involved in the creation and administration of the national park, the use of Spanish names has been encouraged. However, some English names remain popular. All or some of the following islands and localities will be included in your itinerary.

Baltra
   Airport
Bartolomé
Española
   Gardner Bay
   Punta Suarez
Fernandina
   Punta Espinosa
Floreana
   Black Beach
   Post Office Bay
   Punta Cormorante
Genovesa

Isabela
   Tagus Cove
North Seymour
Rabida
Santa Cruz
   Academy Bay
   New Road
   Tortoise Reserve
Santiago (San Salvador)
   Espumillo Beach
   Salt Lake
   South James Bay
   Sullivan Bay
South Plaza

HOW TO USE THIS BOOK

The 87 plants described and illustrated here are the most obvious ones that I have observed along the trails during my trips to the islands. I have included a few introduced plants that have escaped into the native vegetation. Other cultivated plants, which may be observed around settlements, are described briefly in a separate section. Although this guide considers only about 10 percent of the Galápagos flora, it includes 48 plant families and representatives of all vegetation zones.

Plants are organized by the most obvious feature: growth form. There are four categories: trees, shrubs, vines, and herbs (including nonflowering plants). Within each category, plants are arranged by vegetation zones, going from the shore to higher elevations. Within a vegetation zone, species are placed alphabetically by Latin name.

These Latin names may be unfamiliar, but they are necessary to know exactly which plant is being discussed. The same common name often is applied to several different plants in different places. When using Latin names, there is no confusion. The name consists of two parts, the *genus* (comparable to a person's surname—e.g., Smith) and the *species* (comparable to a first name—e.g., John). Then there is an abbreviation of the name of the authority, the person who first described the species.

Groups of related plants that share characteristics in common are placed in *families*, the names of which always end in "aceae"—e.g., Cactaceae. The family names will tell you which of the plants are related.

Only a few Galápagos plants have been given common names, and most of these are Spanish. Therefore, common names have been derived from other areas, a few new ones have been coined, and some follow the tradition of using the Latin name as a common name (e.g., aster, petunia). Wherever possible, both a Spanish and an English name are provided.

Most of the descriptions are derived from the very detailed ones in the *Flora of the Galápagos Islands* by I. L. Wiggins and D. M. Porter (Stanford University Press, 1971). The descriptions here are simple, avoiding excessive use of technical terms. Any words that may be unfamiliar are defined in the glossary. Descriptions include the most noticeable characteristics of the plants: general aspect, branching, bark; leaf shape and arrangement; flower arrangement, shape, structure, and color; fruit shape, color, and texture. Measurements are omitted, since you will not have time to study the plants carefully enough to compare exact sizes.

Distribution information includes the habitat, zone(s), and island(s) where the plant grows, noting the places where it is most abundant and distribution outside the Galápagos, if any. Two categories of plants are marked. *Endemic* plants grow only in the Galápagos and are the most unusual. *Introduced* plants are those that were brought to the islands purposely by humans. All others are considered "native"; that is, they arrived at the islands by natural means and also grow in other areas.

Remarks include any noteworthy or interesting facts about the plant. In cases where several related species grow in the islands, I have chosen a common one to describe and have mentioned the others in this section.

The illustrations are designed to show the features mentioned in the descriptions, including variability of certain characters. To keep the drawings simple, details like hairs have been drawn only on a part of the plant, even though they may occur throughout. These drawings will serve as the primary means of identification for many readers. Just find the right category and zone (e.g., shrubs of the dry zone) and look through the drawings to identify the plant in question.

For those who wish to approach plant identification in a more scientific way, keys are provided. They are organized by the four major groups (trees, shrubs, vines, and herbs). Further subdivisions are made on the basis of leaf and flower characteristics (or others, if necessary).

After the descriptions there are checklists that include the plants I observed on each island. Studying these lists before you visit an island will help you to recognize the plants. Finally, there is space at the back of the book to make notes on the plants (and animals or birds) you see every day and to record other thoughts about your trip.

HOW TO USE THIS BOOK

Littoral Zone. Two common mangrove trees that grow along the shore can be distinguished by color: *Rhizophora* is bright green and *Avicennia* is gray-green.

Littoral Zone. Several herbs, shrubs, and vines grow on sand dunes near the shore.

Dry Zone. The cactus forest on Santa Cruz features two tree cacti, *Opuntia* and *Jasminocereus*, with a dense undergrowth of shrubs and herbs.

Transition Zone. *Bursera* (palo santo) is the characteristic tree, with silvery-gray bark, shown here in its dormant condition during the dry season.

KEY TO TREES

1 Leaves absent.
  2 Branches cylindrical, candelabralike . . . . *Jasminocereus*
  2 Branches flat, oval . . . . *Opuntia echios*

1 Leaves present.
  3 Leaves compound.
    4 Spines present on trunk and branches.
      5 Stalk between leaflets winged . . . . *Zanthoxylum*
      5 Stalk between leaflets not winged.
        6 Central stalk of leaf wide, flat, and green . . . . . *Parkinsonia*
        6 Central stalk of leaf narrow, cylindrical.
          7 Inflorescence round, fluffy, yellow . . . . *Acacia*
          7 Inflorescence elongated, fluffy, greenish-yellow . . . .
          . . . . *Prosopis*
    4 Spines absent.
      8 Trunk and branches silvery gray; leaves clustered at tips
      of branches . . . . *Bursera*
      8 Trunk brown, scaly; leaves (fronds) in whorl at top . . . .
      . . . . *Cyathea*

  3 Leaves simple.
    9 Leaves in clusters near tips of branches.
      10 Leaves oval to narrow, covered with star-shaped
      hairs . . . . *Croton*
      10 Leaves oval to usually triangular with elongated, pointed
      tip, covered with simple hairs . . . . *Scalesia*
    9 Leaves not in clusters.
      11 Leaves opposite.
        12 Leaf surface smooth.
          13 Dots present near margins of leaves . . . *Laguncularia*
          13 Dots absent . . . . *Rhizophora*
        12 Leaf surface hairy.
          14 Leaves triangular with elongated tip . . . . *Scalesia*
          14 Leaves not triangular.
            15 Leaves narrowly oblong . . . . *Avicennia*
            15 Leaves oval.

16 Leaf surface with glands (dots).....*Psidium*

16 Leaf surface without glands.

    17 Leaves hairy on both sides; flowers in small heads.................*Scalesia*

    17 Leaves hairy underneath; flowers in much-branched inflorescences........

    ....*Cinchona*

11 Leaves alternate.

  18 Leaf surface smooth.

    19 Leaves narrow.....................*Bambusa*

    19 Leaves oval to round.

      20 Flowers in long spikes; fruits yellow, not opening

      ....*Hippomane*

      20 Flowers in clusters; fruits reddish, opening into 3 parts.................*Maytenus*

  18 Leaf surface hairy.

    21 Leaves narrow.

      22 Hairs sparse, simple.................*Bambusa*

      22 Hairs dense, star-shaped.............*Croton*

    21 Leaves broad.

      23 Leaf surface covered with star-shaped hairs.....

      ....*Croton*

      23 Leaf surface covered with simple hairs.

        24 Leaves triangular with elongated tip........

        ....*Scalesia*

        24 Leaves oval to round.

          25 Leaves bearing glands on lower surface

          ....*Conocarpus*

          25 Leaves without glands.

            26 Leaf margins lobed; lower surface hairy.................*Ochroma*

            26 Leaf margins entire; both surfaces hairy.

              27 Flowers white, in small heads....

              ....*Scalesia*

              27 Flowers yellow, in branched inflorescences...........*Cordia*

KEY TO SHRUBS

1 Leaves absent.
  2 Branches wide, flat, oval, and green . . . . *Opuntia helleri*
  2 Branches narrow, cylindrical.
    3 Side branches ending in a spiny tip . . . . *Lycium*
    3 Side branches bearing many sharp spines . . . . *Scutia*

1 Leaves present.
  4 Leaves compound.
    5 Branches smooth . . . . *Cassia*
    5 Branches bearing prickles and curved spines . . . . . . *Caesalpinia*
  4 Leaves simple.
    6 Leaves arranged in whorls or clusters.
      7 Leaves in whorls of 3 . . . . *Clerodendrum*
      7 Leaves in clusters.
        8 Branches bearing spines . . . . *Grabowskia*
        8 Branches lacking spines.
          9 Tips of side branches sharply pointed . . . . *Lycium*
          9 Tips of side branches not pointed.
            10 Leaves succulent, club-shaped . . . . *Nolana*
            10 Leaves not succulent, narrow.
              11 Flower heads usually on short stalks, in clusters
              . . . . *Darwiniothamnus*
              11 Flower heads usually on long stalks, single
              . . . . *Macraea*
    6 Leaves not in whorls or clusters.
      12 Leaves opposite.
        13 Leaves lobed . . . . *Lecocarpus*
        13 Leaves not lobed.
          14 Margins of leaves toothed . . . . *Lantana*
          14 Margins of leaves not toothed.
            15 Leaves with 3 prominent parallel veins . . . . *Miconia*
            15 Leaves without parallel veins.
              16 Leaves narrow.
                17 Leaves leathery, needlelike . . . . *Macraea*

       17 Leaves fleshy....................*Batis*

    16 Leaves elliptic to oval.

       18 Leaves with obvious dots along margins

       ....*Laguncularia*

       18 Leaves lacking dots.

         19 Leaves covered with star-shaped hairs..

         ....*Alternanthera*

         19 Leaves lacking star-shaped hairs.

           20 Flowers white, short-tubular.......

           ....*Chiococca*

           20 Flowers white, long-slender-tubular

           ....*Clerodendrum*

12 Leaves alternate.

  21 Surface of leaves mealy....................*Atriplex*

  21 Surface of leaves not mealy.

    22 Leaves with lobes.

      23 Leaves palmately lobed..............*Ricinus*

      23 Leaves with 3 shallow lobes.

        24 Leaf surface covered with black dots.......

        ....*Gossypium*

        24 Leaf surface covered with star-shaped hairs

        ....*Waltheria*

    22 Leaves without lobes.

      25 Leaves heart-shaped.

        26 Leaf surface covered with simple hairs

        ....*Cryptocarpus*

        26 Leaf surface covered with star-shaped hairs..

        ....*Waltheria*

      25 Leaves not heart-shaped.

        27 Margins of leaves toothed.

          28 Leaves narrow or oblong.......*Castela*

          28 Leaves usually oval.

            29 Surface of leaf smooth....*Maytenus*

            29 Surface of leaf covered with star-

            shaped hairs............*Waltheria*

        27 Margins of leaves not toothed.

          30 Surface of leaves hairy.

            31 Leaves narrowly elliptic to oblong

            ....*Vallesia*

            31 Leaves elliptic, oval to round.

                                                KEY TO SHRUBS

32 Leaves elliptic to oval; flowers small, yellowish, on long curved inflorescences . . . . . . *Tournefortia*

32 Leaves oval to round; flowers large, bright yellow, on branched inflorescences . . . . *Cordia*

30 Surface of leaves not hairy.

33 Branches bearing spines.

34 Leaves oval . . . . *Grabowskia*

34 Leaves narrow to oblong.

35 Spines short; flowers red . . . . *Castela*

35 Spines long; flowers yellowish . . . . *Scutia*

33 Branches lacking spines.

36 Leaves round, fleshy . . . . *Scaevola*

36 Leaves not round or fleshy.

37 Leaves oval . . . . . . *Maytenus*

37 Leaves not oval.

38 Leaves very narrow.

39 Flowers white . . . . *Lycium*

39 Flower heads yellow . . . . . . *Darwiniothamnus*

38 Leaves narrowly elliptic to oblong . . . . *Vallesia*

KEY TO VINES

1 Leaves simple.
   2 Leaves triangular, flowers white . . . . *Ipomoea habeliana*
   2 Leaves heart-shaped, flowers pink . . . . *Ipomoea triloba*

1 Leaves lobed or divided.
   3 Leaves divided into 5 fingerlike segments . . . . *Merremia*
   3 Leaves 3-lobed.
      4 Flowers pink, tubular . . . . *Ipomoea triloba*
      4 Flowers white and purple, petals separate . . . . *Passiflora*

Note: Several plants with trailing stems may be confused with true vines. These are described in their proper category:
   Shrubs: *Cryptocarpus* and *Tournefortia*
   Herbs: *Cacabus, Lycopodium, Sesuvium, Tribulus,* and *Vigna*

KEY TO HERBS

1 Leaves absent.
  2 Branches thick, brownish, spiny . . . . *Brachycereus*
  2 Branches thin, gray, bumpy . . . . *Roccella*

1 Leaves present.
  3 Leaves compound.
    4 Leaves with 2 segments, close to stem.
      5 Plants green or red, floating on water . . . . *Azolla*
      5 Plants brown, growing on trees . . . . *Frullania*
    4 Leaves with more than 2 segments, spreading.
      6 Leaves with 3 leaflets.
        7 Leaflets broadly oval to narrow, margins entire . . . .
        . . . . *Vigna*
        7 Leaflets oval to diamond-shaped, margins toothed . . . .
        . . . . *Bidens*
      6 Leaves with many leaflets.
        8 Leaflets with entire margins . . . . *Tribulus*
        8 Leaflets with toothed or lobed margins.
          9 Leaflets with toothed margins . . . . *Bidens*
          9 Leaflets with lobed margins.
            10 Top margin only of leaflets lobed . . . . *Adiantum*
            10 Both margins of leaflet lobed.
              11 Lobes deep and even . . . . *Pteridium*
              11 Lobes shallow and irregular . . . . . . *Lycopersicon*

  3 Leaves simple.
    12 Leaves arranged in spirals or whorls.
      13 Leaves spirally arranged on candelabralike branches . . . . .
      . . . . *Lycopodium*
      13 Leaves arranged in whorls around branched stems . . . .
      . . . . *Mollugo*
    12 Leaves not arranged in whorls or spirals.
      14 Leaves alternate.
        15 Leaves with 3 lobes.

16 Flowers white . . . . *Anoda*

16 Flowers yellow . . . . *Mentzelia*

15 Leaves without lobes.

    17 Leaves long and linear.

        18 Flowers in a whorled inflorescence . . . . *Cyperus*

        18 Flowers in a long spike . . . . *Pennisetum*

    17 Leaves shorter and more broad.

        19 Surface of leaf smooth.

            20 Margins of leaf wavy and bearing glands
                . . . . *Porophyllum*

            20 Margins of leaf entire and lacking glands.

                21 Flowers in axils of leaves . . . . . *Capsicum*

                21 Flowers in spikes at ends of branches.

                    22 Flowers 2-parted, usually lavender
                        . . . . *Polygala*

                    22 Flowers long-tubular, white . . . .
                        . . . . *Plumbago*

        19 Surface of leaf hairy.

            23 Margins of leaf entire.

                24 Leaves clustered; flowers single among
                    leaves . . . . *Tiquilia*

                24 Leaves distributed along stems; flowers
                    in long, curving inflorescences . . . .
                    . . . . *Heliotropium*

            23 Margins of leaf wavy or toothed.

                25 Surface of leaf covered with star-shaped
                    hairs . . . . *Sida*

                25 Surface of leaf covered with simple hairs.

                    26 Leaves oval.

                      27 Flowers on erect stalks . . . .
                        . . . . *Mentzelia*

                      27 Flowers on drooping stalks.

                        28 Flowers single, yellow . . . . . .
                          . . . . *Physalis*

                      28 Flowers in whorls, white . . . .
                        . . . . *Solanum*

                    26 Leaves not oval.

                      29 Leaves shield-shaped . . . .
                      . . . . *Cacabus*

                      29 Leaves angular.

30 Leaves diamond-shaped;
flowers in whorls on drooping stalks . . . . *Solanum*

30 Leaves triangular; flowers
single, on erect stems . . . .
. . . . *Anoda*

14 Leaves opposite.

31 Surface of leaf smooth.

32 Leaf margins wavy; glands usually present near
margin . . . . *Porophyllum*

32 Leaf margins entire; glands absent.

33 Leaves noticeably fleshy.

34 Leaves narrow to oblong; surface usually
with tiny dots . . . . *Sesuvium*

34 Leaves oval to round, dots absent.

35 Pairs of leaves equal in size; flowers
yellow . . . . *Portulaca*

35 Pairs of leaves unequal in size; flowers
purplish . . . . *Trianthema*

33 Leaves not fleshy.

36 Leaves small, round with heart-shaped base;
flowers in greenish, cup-shaped structures
. . . . *Chamaesyce*

36 Leaves larger, oval to round with heart-
shaped base; flowers in branched inflorescence, reddish-purple . . . . . *Commicarpus*

31 Leaf surface hairy.

37 Leaf margins entire.

38 Leaves very narrow, with glands underneath
. . . . *Pectis*

38 Leaves broader, glands absent.

39 Leaves oval to elliptic; flowers in
branched inflorescence, purple . . . .
. . . . *Justicia*

39 Leaves oval; flowers in tight clusters,
white . . . . *Borreria*

37 Leaf margins wavy or toothed.

40 Leaves narrow to oblong . . . . *Verbena*

40 Leaves broader.

41 Leaves shield-shaped . . . . *Cacabus*
41 Leaves not shield-shaped.
    42 Leaves oval.
        43 Flowers in long spikes . . . .
        . . . . *Salvia*
        43 Flowers in heads.
            44 Flowers blue to pink (sometimes white); fruits wedge-shaped . . . . *Eupatorium*
            44 Flowers yellowish; fruits narrow with barbed projections . . . . *Bidens*
    42 Leaves angular.
        45 Leaves triangular . . . *Eupatorium*
        45 Leaves diamond-shaped.
            46 Flowers in long spikes, blue
            . . . . *Salvia*
            46 Flowers in heads, yellowish
            . . . . *Bidens*

inflorescence — the arrangement and order of development of flowers on an axis.

KEY TO HERBS

The cloud cover above 3,000 feet provides moisture for the wet forest and shrub zones.

Scalesia Zone.
A rare tree of the daisy family, *Scalesia* grows at higher elevations around old craters on Santa Cruz. A Galápagos tree fern can be seen halfway up the cliff.

Miconia Zone. The shrub *Miconia* is dominant, with an undergrowth of bracken fern (foreground) and other herbs.

Fern Sedge Zone. Best developed on Santa Cruz, this zone features ferns, sedges, grasses, and other herbs.

Avicennia germinans (L.) L.
Avicenniaceae   Mangle Negro, Black Mangrove

Tree with spreading branches, thin aerial rootstocks projecting from soil around trunk; *leaves* opposite, narrowly oblong, covered beneath with whitish hairs; *inflorescences* branched, at tips of branches; *flowers* small, petals whitish, hairy, united into tube at base and spreading into 4 small lobes above; *fruits* dry, oval, hairy, yellowish. *Distribution*: Along coasts of several islands, especially near lagoons at Espumillo Beach (Santiago) and at Punta Cormorante (Floreana); also distributed in the American tropics.

   Remarks: This species has the highest salt tolerance of any mangrove in the Galápagos. There are special glands on the leaves to excrete salt. The projecting rootstocks take in air. Its grayish-green color easily distinguishes this tree from the dark green *Rhizophora*, often growing in the same areas.

Conocarpus erecta L.
Combretaceae   Mangle Boton, Button Mangrove

Tree, usually small, with spreading, hairy branches; *leaves* alternate, oval to elliptic, leathery, usually hairy and bearing glands underneath; *inflorescences* at ends of branches, consisting of dense round heads; *flowers* small, sepals 5, greenish, no petals, usually 5 stamens in center; *fruits* dry, brown, small, in conelike clusters. *Distribution*: Near the shores of several islands, especially along lagoons at Espumillo Beach (Santiago); also distributed in tropical America and Africa.

Remarks: This less common mangrove usually grows in areas of lower salt concentration than the others.

Laguncularia racemosa. See SHRUBS OF THE LITTORAL ZONE.

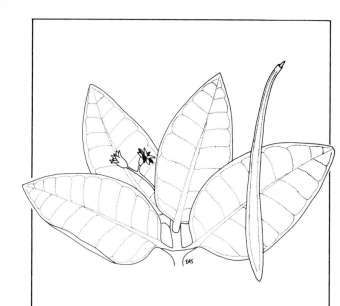

Rhizophora mangle L.
Rhizophoraceae   Mangle Rojo, Red Mangrove

Tree with prominent prop roots extending into salt water; *leaves* opposite, oval to elliptic, thick, dark green; *flowers* in pairs on short branches among the leaves, calyx of 4 yellow-green lobes, petals 4, separate, white; *fruits* fleshy, oval, green, germinating while still attached to the plant into long bean-shaped structures. *Distribution:* Along the shores of several islands, especially noticeable at Punta Espinosa (Fernandina) and Academy Bay (Santa Cruz); also distributed around the world.

Remarks: This is the most common of the mangroves. Fruits drop into the mud and start to grow immediately, so the trees spread easily. The fruits also are able to float in the ocean, accounting for the wide distribution. The roots filter out salt so that nearly pure water is transported to the leaves.

TREES OF THE DRY ZONE

Acacia macracantha Willd.

Mimosaceae   Algarrobo, Acacia

Tree with long, sharp spines on branches at base of leaves; *leaves* alternate, doubly compound, leaflets opposite, oval, numerous, and close together, sometimes with hairs on margins; *inflorescences* round, fluffy, on stalks in axils of leaves; *flowers* small, petals yellow, fused below, and separating into 5 lobes above, many stamens protruding; *fruits* dry, narrow, elongate, flat, and somewhat curved. *Distribution:* In dry areas on major islands, noticeable at Academy Bay (Santa Cruz), Espumillo Beach and South James Bay (Santiago); also distributed in the Caribbean and South America.

Remarks: This is one of four species of acacia in the Galápagos. All are very similar and may be found growing together. They have in common the compound leaves, spines, and round, yellow balls of flowers.

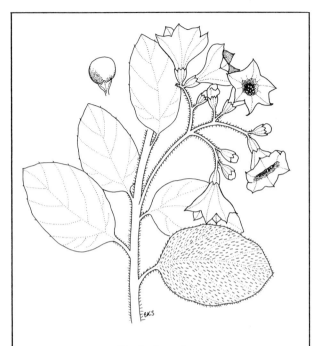

Cordia lutea Lam.
Boraginaceae   Muyuyo, Yellow Cordia

Tree or shrub with smooth, light gray bark, smaller branches hairy; *leaves* alternate, egg-shaped to nearly round, margins slightly irregular, hairs on surface; *inflorescences* curved and branched; *flowers* large, calyx cup-shaped, and ribbed on sides, petals bright yellow, fused into a short tube that expands into 5–6 broad, pointed lobes at top; *fruits* oval and dry. *Distribution:* Dry areas on nearly all islands; shrubby form common on Genovesa; tree form on Santiago, at Tagus Cove (Isabela), and Academy Bay (Santa Cruz); also distributed in western South America.

Remarks: This is one of the most spectacular Galápagos plants, with its abundant, brilliant yellow flowers visible from a distance.

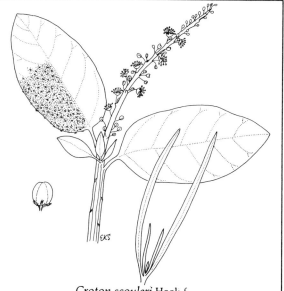

Croton scouleri Hook.f.
Euphorbiaceae   Chala, Croton

Tree, slender, small, with smooth, pale bark; *leaves* alternate, sometimes clustered near tips of branches, broadly oval to very narrow, covered with star-shaped hairs; *inflorescences* long spikes of small flowers at ends of branches; *male flowers* with 5 greenish petals and cluster of stamens in center, *female flowers* with 5 hairy sepals, usually no petals, round pistil in center; *fruits* round, dry, 3-lobed, and splitting into sections. *Distribution:* Widely distributed in islands, from dry areas to higher elevations; broad-leaved form seen on Genovesa, narrow-leaved form at Tagus Cove (Isabela) and South James Bay (Santiago). ENDEMIC.

   Remarks: Early collectors assigned different names to *Croton* plants with different shapes of leaves. Recent study has shown that there is a gradual change from narrow to broad leaves in one species, with many intermediates to be found. This variation probably is related to environmental conditions.

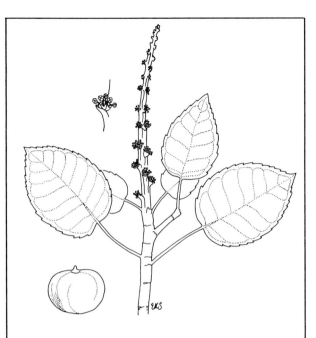

Hippomane mancinella L.
Euphorbiaceae   Manzanillo, Manchineel

Tree with rounded shape, smooth branches, and irritating sap; *leaves* alternate, broadly oval, slightly toothed margins; *inflorescences* long spikes at ends of branches; *flowers* small, in clusters, sepals greenish, no petals; *fruits* fleshy, resembling small, yellowish apples. *Distribution:* Near the shore or at higher elevations on several islands, usually seen at Academy Bay (Santa Cruz) and behind lagoons at Espumillo Beach (Santiago); also distributed from the Caribbean to South America. POISONOUS.

Remarks: This is the only native poisonous plant in the Galápagos. The sap causes dermatitis, and eating several fruits can be fatal. Native birds and animals do not eat them either, for the ground beneath the trees is always littered with fruits.

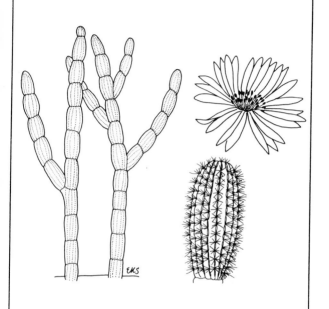

Jasminocereus thouarsii (Weber) Backbg.
Cactaceae   Cirio, Candelabra Cactus

Tree with straight trunk and cylindrical, erect branches, divided into sections, surface ribbed and covered with clusters of spines; *no leaves; flowers* solitary on branches, sepals many, reddish, petals many, yellow or greenish, many stamens in center; *fruits* fleshy, round or oval, green to reddish. *Distribution:* At low elevations on several islands, especially common at Academy Bay (Santa Cruz), also Punta Cormorante (Floreana). ENDEMIC.

Maytenus octogona. See SHRUBS OF THE DRY ZONE.

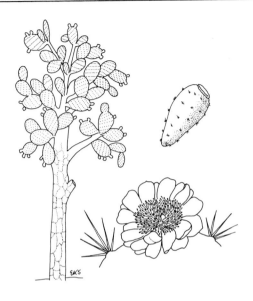

Opuntia echios Howell
Cactaceae   Tuna, Giant Prickly Pear

Tree with straight trunk, spiny when young, covered with reddish-brown bark when mature; branches at top, curving downward, with many green, oval *pads*, covered with clusters of spines; *no leaves; flowers* solitary, large, at tips of pads, sepals many, greenish, petals many, yellow, many stamens in center; *fruits* top-shaped, green or reddish, fleshy. *Distribution:* From sea level to middle elevations on several islands, especially South Plaza and at Academy Bay (Santa Cruz). ENDEMIC.

Remarks: This tree cactus is one of the most distinctive Galápagos plants. The development of the tree form was influenced by several factors, including competition of cactus seedlings with others for light and grazing pressure from tortoises. There are other similar tree species of *Opuntia*, also endemic, on several other islands.

thorn

Parkinsonia aculeata L.
Caesalpiniaceae   Palo Verde

Tree with arching branches, sometimes near the ground, short spines on branches at base of leaves; *leaves* alternate, compound, with expanded, long, and curving stalks, leaflets tiny, alternate, oblong to elliptic, and falling off easily; *inflorescences* branched, in axils of leaves; *flowers* showy, petals 5, yellow, separate, the upper one larger and with a red-orange spot at the base, cluster of 10 stamens in center; *fruits* dry, elongated, covered with small white dots. *Distribution:* At low elevations, often on sand, on several islands, especially near lagoons at Punta Cormorante (Floreana) and at Academy Bay (Santa Cruz); also widely distributed from southwestern United States to Argentina.

Remarks: The Spanish common name for this tree means "green stick," and refers to the long green stalks that are often seen without leaflets.

N. Seymour- only one
on two flowering sections rest without

Prosopis juliflora (Sw.) DC.
Mimosaceae   Mesquite

Tree with sharp spines on branches at base of leaves; *leaves* alternate, compound, usually in 2 parts, leaflets opposite, oblong, usually rather widely spaced; *inflorescences* long, fluffy spikes, on stalks in axils of leaves; *flowers* small, petals 5, separate, greenish-yellow, usually 10 stamens protruding; *fruits* dry, elongated, sometimes curved. *Distribution:* In dry areas on major islands, most obvious at Punta Cormorante (Floreana); also distributed from Mexico to South America.

Remarks: This tree can be distinguished easily from its thorny relative *Acacia* by the paired, singly compound leaves and long inflorescences.

TREES OF THE
TRANSITION ZONE

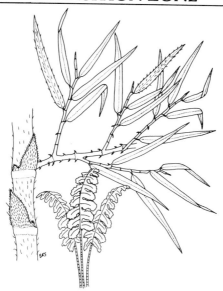

Bambusa guadua H. & B.
Poaceae   Caña Guadua, Giant Bamboo

Tree with tall, slender trunk and many branches, growing in clumps and resembling giant plumes, trunks green with white bands, stiff hairs and alternate, triangular sheaths, branches covered with thorns; *leaves* on side branches, alternate, long, narrowly oval to very narrow, bases wrapped around branches, surface smooth or with a few stiff hairs; *flowers* small, surrounded by several bracts, on leafless branches, usually not seen; *fruits* usually not seen. *Distribution:* From middle to higher elevations along the New Road on Santa Cruz. IN-TRODUCED.

Remarks: This tree member of the grass family is widely grown in Ecuador for use in house construction. It may have been introduced to the islands more than once and appears to be invading native forest.

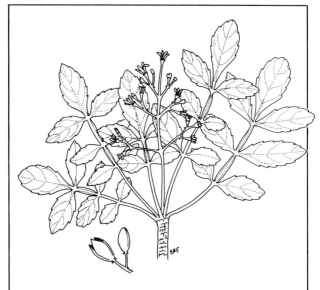

Bursera graveolens (HBK) Trian. & Planch.
Burseraceae   Palo Santo, Incense Tree

Tree with widely spreading branches, silvery-gray bark;
leaves clustered at tips of branches, compound, leaflets opposite, oval with pointed tips and toothed margins; *inflorescences* branched, among leaves; *flowers* small, petals 4, separate, whitish; *fruits* oval, brown, dry, opening into 2-3 sections. *Distribution:* Common on most islands at low elevations, especially obvious at Tagus Cove (Isabela) and on Santiago; also distributed in Mexico and western South America.

Remarks: This tree is related to frankincense and contains
an aromatic resin. Branches are burned for incense in
churches, hence the common name, meaning "holy stick." For
much of the year palo santo is without leaves (to conserve
water), but is easily recognized by the silvery color of the
trunk and branches. Another species, *B. malacophylla,* is EN-
DEMIC. It is smaller, somewhat twisted in shape and its leaves
are grayish-green. It grows only on three small islands and can
be observed on North Seymour.

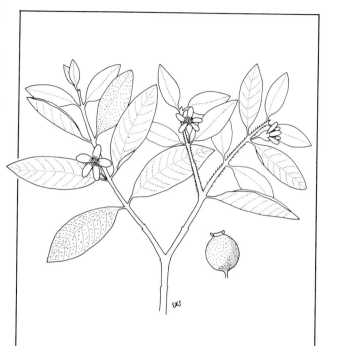

Psidium galapageium Hook.f.
Myrtaceae Guayabillo, Galápagos Guava

Tree with smooth, gray bark, small branches hairy; *leaves* opposite, elliptic to oval, surfaces somewhat hairy and dotted with glands; *flowers* solitary in axils of leaves, petals 5, white, separate, with prominent cluster of white stamens in center; *fruits* round, fleshy, yellow, with persistent calyx on top. *Distribution:* In moister forests on major islands, best observed along the New Road on Santa Cruz. ENDEMIC.

Remarks: The cultivated guava (*P. guajava* L.) has escaped into native forests on three islands and also may be seen on Santa Cruz. It is similar, but taller, with larger leaves, flowers, and fruits.

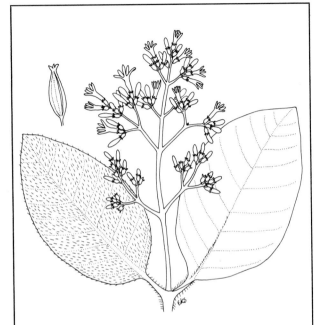

Cinchona succiruba Pav. ex Klotsch.
Rubiaceae   Cascarilla, Quinine

Tree, tall, with reddish bark that can be peeled off; *leaves* opposite, oval to elliptic, large, usually hairy underneath; *inflorescences* much-branched, at ends of branches; *flowers* small, rosy-pink, petals tubular at base, separating into 5 lobes at top; *fruits* dry, opening to release winged seeds. *Distribution:* In wet forest zone on Santa Cruz; also at high elevations in Ecuador and Peru. INTRODUCED.

Remarks: This tree has caused much damage by taking over areas that should be occupied by *Scalesia* and other native species. National Park personnel have been working to cut down the offensive trees. The inner layer of bark yields quinine, the famous cure for malaria.

Cyathea weatherbyana (Morton) Morton
Cyatheaceae   Chontillo, Galápagos Tree Fern

Tree with thick trunk, upper part covered with scales; *fronds* in whorls near top of trunk, large, compound, segments alternate, narrow, with lobed margins, hairy underneath; *no flowers; fruiting bodies* round, near edges of frond segments on underside. *Distribution:* Growing in craters and gullies at high elevations on several islands, observed on Santa Cruz in *Scalesia* forest near Los Hermanos close to the New Road. ENDEMIC.

Remarks: Although tree ferns are quite abundant on Santa Cruz, they have been badly damaged on other islands by cattle grazing and need protection.

Ochroma pyramidale (Cav. ex Lam.) Urban
Bombacaceae   Balsa

Tree with tall, straight trunk, bark mottled with white, branches only at the top; *leaves* alternate, oval to nearly round, base heart-shaped and a shallow lobe on each side, brown hairs on underside; *flowers* large, solitary in axils of leaves, petals white, separate but forming a funnel with 5 broad lobes at top, stamens fused into hollow tube in center; *fruits* dry, woody, narrow to oblong, opening to show many seeds covered with brown, silky fibers. *Distribution:* At higher elevations in Santa Cruz, invading the *Scalesia* forest; also distributed in Mexico, Central America to Bolivia. INTRODUCED.

Remarks: Balsa trees were brought to the Galápagos in 1940 but never were developed into a profitable export. Since being abandoned, they have continued to spread into the native forest.

Another tree in the same family also has escaped cultivation. *Ceiba pentandra* (L.) Gaertn. is the source of the fiber kapok, derived from the seeds. This tree differs from balsa in having spines on the branches and leaves palmately divided. The fruits are similar, opening to release seeds bearing large masses of silky hairs.

Scalesia pedunculata Hook.f.
Asteraceae   Lechoso, Daisy Tree

Tree with straight trunk and crown of curving branches; *leaves* alternate or opposite, usually clustered at ends of branches, lower ones dying off, oval to triangular with elongate, pointed tip, margins usually entire, sometimes toothed, surface covered with hairs; *flower heads* at ends of branches on long stalks, bracts numerous and hairy, rays absent, disk flowers prominent, whitish; *fruits* dry, flat, usually lacking bristles. *Distribution:* Forming forests in wet zones of larger islands, usually seen along the New Road in vicinity of Los Hermanos (Santa Cruz). ENDEMIC.

Remarks: This is one of the few trees in the family Asteraceae, which includes such familiar plants as daisies, sunflowers, and asters. It is also the most important of the Galápagos endemics, still not studied adequately by botanists. Although expanses of forest survive on Santa Cruz, the trees are much threatened by human activity.

Low-growing mat plants, like *Chamaesyce*, stabilize the sandy soil.

Succulent herbs are common in the dry zone. *Trianthema* can be recognized by its red stems and white flowers.

The green pads of *Opuntia* cactus are covered with sharp spines.

Galápagos cotton *(Gossypium)* shrubs have the most conspicuous flowers in the upper vegetation zones.

Zanthoxylum fagara (L.) Sarg.
Rutaceae   Uña de Gato, Prickly Ash

Tree with light gray bark, branches with pairs of hooked spines, younger branches hairy; *leaves* alternate, compound, stem between leaflets winged, leaflets opposite, terminal one sometimes missing, oval or broadly elliptic, shiny dark green, margins lobed; *inflorescences* clusters of male or female flowers in axils of leaves; *male and female flowers* similar, petals 4, whitish, oval; *fruits* dry, oval, covered with dark dots. *Distribution:* From low to high elevations on most islands, often seen under *Scalesia* trees near Los Hermanos, the New Road (Santa Cruz); also distributed from southern United States to Peru.

SHRUBS OF THE LITTORAL ZONE

Atriplex peruviana Moq.
Chenopodiaceae   Mealy Leaf

Shrub, much branched; *leaves* alternate, oval to triangular, surface mealy; *inflorescences* spikes with clusters of small flowers, mostly at ends of branches; *male flowers* with 5 sepals, greenish, no petals, *female flowers* with 2 bracts, no sepals or petals; *fruits* dry, enclosed by enlarged bracts. *Distribution:* Near the shore on a few islands, most obvious in community of salt-tolerant plants at Punta Suarez (Española); also known in Peru and Chile.

Batis maritima L.
Batidaceae   Saltwort

Shrub, much branched, stems trailing or upright; *leaves* opposite, narrow, fleshy; *inflorescences* fleshy, conelike, in axils of leaves; *male and female flowers* separate, small, greenish, cup-shaped; *fruits* irregularly rounded, fleshy. *Distribution:* On sand and around salt-water lagoons on several islands, behind beach at Sullivan Bay, and at edge of Salt Lake (Santiago): also distributed in the New World tropics and Hawaii.

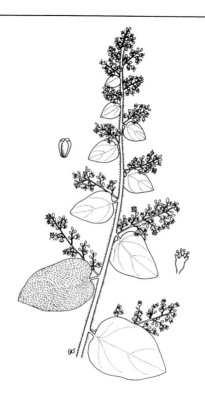

Cryptocarpus pyriformis HBK
Nyctaginaceae   Monte Salado, Salt Bush

Shrub with trailing, hairy branches; *leaves* alternate, heart-shaped, hairy; *inflorescences* long, much-branched, in axils of leaves; *flowers* small, sepals 5, greenish, fused at base, no petals, 4 stamens protruding; *fruits* dry, pear-shaped with 5 sections. *Distribution:* Abundant near the coast of all islands, especially obvious at Academy Bay (Santa Cruz), Genovesa, Punta Cormorante (Floreana), Punta Suarez (Española), and Rabida; also known in Ecuador and Peru.

Laguncularia racemosa (L.) Gaertn.
Combretaceae   Mangle Blanco, White Mangrove

Shrub or small tree, with rounded shape and spreading branches; *leaves* opposite, oval, leathery, with noticeable dots near margins; *inflorescences* short-branched spikes; *flowers* inconspicuous, whitish, hairy; *fruits* dry, greenish, flask-shaped. *Distribution:* Near the shore on sand or lava on several islands, at Punta Espinosa (Fernandina) and near lagoons at Espumillo Beach (Santiago); also distributed in tropical areas around the world.

   Remarks: This member of the mangrove community is not very common and is found farther inland than the red or black mangroves.

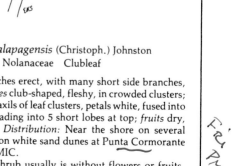

Nolana galapagensis (Christoph.) Johnston
Nolanaceae   Clubleaf

Shrub, main branches erect, with many short side branches, usually hairy; *leaves* club-shaped, fleshy, in crowded clusters; *flowers* solitary in axils of leaf clusters, petals white, fused into a tube below, spreading into 5 short lobes at top; *fruits* dry, small, in clusters. *Distribution:* Near the shore on several islands, abundant on white sand dunes at Punta Cormorante (Floreana). ENDEMIC.

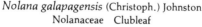

Remarks: This shrub usually is without flowers or fruits, but it is recognizable by the unique fleshy leaves.

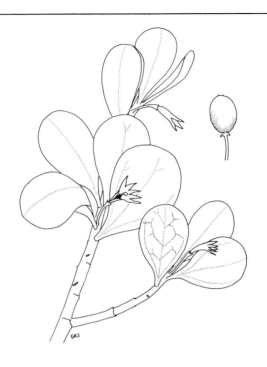

Scaevola plumieri (L.) M. Vahl
Goodeniaceae   Inkberry

Shrub with some trailing branches; *leaves* alternate, oval to nearly round, fleshy, dark green; *flowers* solitary or in groups of 2–3 in axils of leaves, petals white, fused into tube below and separating into 5 narrow lobes at top, appearing as if half of flower missing; *fruits* oval to round, smooth, black, fleshy. *Distribution:* On beaches of Floreana and Isabela, but likely to spread, observed on white sand dunes at Punta Cormorante (Floreana); also widely distributed in tropics around the world.

   Remarks: The fruits of this shrub can float in salt water, accounting for its presence on beaches in most tropical areas.

SHRUBS OF THE DRY ZONE

Cassia picta G. Don
Caesalpiniaceae   Casia, Senna

Shrub with smooth branches; *leaves* alternate, compound, leaflets opposite, oblong with pointed tip; *inflorescences* branched, in axils of leaves or at ends of branches; *flowers* showy, petals 5, bright yellow, separate, 3 upper ones slightly smaller than 2 lower ones, stamens 6, dark brown, 2 of them larger and curved upward; *fruits* dry, elongated, flat, and nearly straight. *Distribution:* On lava or in clearings from sea level to middle elevations on major islands, most often seen on Santiago, in dense stands at edge of woods behind lagoons at Espumillo Beach and along trail at South James Bay; also distributed in Ecuador and Peru.

Remarks: There are several other species of *Cassia* that differ in shape of leaflets, hairiness, and shape of fruit. However, they can be recognized by the distinctive flowers.

EAS

Castela galapageia Hook.f.
Simaroubaceae   Amargo, Bitterbush

Shrub with many branches, often close to ground, younger branches hairy and with short spines, side branches with spiny tips; *leaves* alternate, usually in clusters, oblong, elliptic or narrow, shiny green on top, hairy beneath, margins somewhat wavy or with a few teeth; *flowers* in clusters in axils of leaves, petals 4, separate, red outside and yellow inside, 8 stamens in center; *fruits* oval, fleshy, green turning red. *Distribution:* In dry areas on lava or cinders on most islands, noticeable on Santiago at South James Bay, Espumillo Beach and trail to Salt Lake, on South Plaza, at Academy Bay (Santa Cruz) and Punta Cormorante (Floreana). ENDEMIC.

Remarks: Probably because of its bitter taste, this is one of the few shrubs that is not eaten by goats.

Cordia lutea. See Trees of the Dry Zone.

Grabowskia boerhaaviaefolia (L.f.) Schlecht.
Solanaceae   Desert Plum

Shrub with stiff branches, younger ones with whitish bark, bearing sharp spines and often covered with greenish lichens; *leaves* alternate, sometimes in clusters, oval, smooth; branched *inflorescences* or solitary flowers in axils of leaves; *flowers* white, petals fused at base and separating into 5 lobes at top, stamens 5, protruding from petals; *fruits* dry, oval, dark blue, with waxy coating. *Distribution:* At low elevations on several islands, best observed on South Plaza and at Punta Suarez (Española); also known from Peru.

   Remarks: Like other shrubs at Punta Suarez, this one is seen sometimes without leaves or flowers. It can be recognized by the whitish bark and the growth of lichens on the branches.

Lantana peduncularis Anderss.
Verbenaceae   Lantana

Shrub with slender, 4-angled branches, young twigs hairy; *leaves* opposite, oval to elliptic, margins toothed, surface often covered with fine hairs; *inflorescences* dense heads on long stalks in axils of leaves, hairy bracts below flowers; *flowers* small, petals white, fused into narrow tube and spreading into 5 flat lobes at top, lower middle lobe often larger; *fruits* small, fleshy. *Distribution:* At low elevations, often on lava, on most islands, observed at Tagus Cove (Isabela), Punta Cormorante (Floreana), and Genovesa. ENDEMIC.

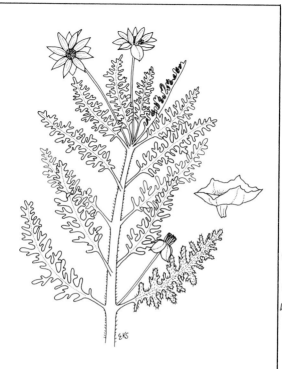

Lecocarpus pinnatifidus Decne.
Asteraceae   Cutleaf Daisy

Shrub of rounded shape with many hairy branches; *leaves* opposite, elliptic, margins deeply and irregularly lobed, surface hairy; *flower heads* single, on stalks near tips of branches, bracts spreading, rays conspicuous, yellow, disks yellow; *fruits* dry, topped by a flaring wing. *Distribution:* Known only at low elevations on Floreana, observed at Punta Cormorante. ENDEMIC.

Remarks: This is one of the most restricted of Galápagos plants. Two other endemic species of *Lecocarpus* are distributed on three other islands.

SHRUBS OF DRY ZONE

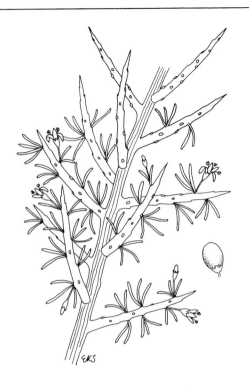

EKS

Lycium minimum C.L. Hitchc.
Solanaceae   Desert-thorn

Shrub with many erect branches, bark with fine stripes, side
branches short, stiff, and pointed; *leaves* narrow, in alternate
bundles of 2–5; *flowers* in axils of leaves, petals usually 4,
white, turning brown, yellow anthers protruding; *fruits*
fleshy, oval, reddish. *Distribution:* Near coast of several
islands, an obvious part of the scrub vegetation at Punta
Suarez (Espanola). ENDEMIC.

Remarks: This shrub loses its leaves, flowers, and fruits
readily and often appears as a tangle of spine-tipped branches.

Macraea laricifolia Hook.f.
Asteraceae   Romerillo, Needle-leaf Daisy

Shrub with slender, curving branches, the younger ones hairy; *leaves* opposite or in clusters, very narrow and leathery, hairy, especially underneath; *flower heads* single, on stalks at ends of branches, rays small, yellow, disks yellow; *fruits* triangular, dry, rough on surface and winged on sides. *Distribution:* Growing from sea level to higher elevations on major islands, best observed near top of trail at Tagus Cove (Isabela). ENDEMIC.

Remarks: In the dry season, this shrub will appear as curving branches bearing a few dried, needlelike leaves and dried flower heads.

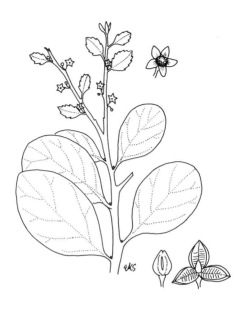

Maytenus octogona (L'Her.) DC.
Celastraceae   Arrayancillo, Leather Leaf

Shrub or small tree, branches often drooping; *leaves* alternate, round, oval or elliptic, light green, younger ones with toothed margins, leathery or fleshy; *flowers* in clusters in axils of leaves, very small, petals 4, separate, green, stamens 5; *fruits* dry, reddish, oval, breaking into 3 parts to reveal pulpy red seeds. *Distribution:* Common near the coast on most islands, less common at higher elevations on lava, observed on South Plaza, Sullivan Bay (Santiago), at Punta Cormorante (Floreana) and Punta Espinosa (Fernandina); also distributed in western South America.

   Remarks: This coastal shrub is recognized easily by its bright yellow-green color and the stiff leaves, often in a vertical position to avoid the direct sun.

Opuntia helleri K. Schum.
Cactaceae   Tuna, Prickly Pear

Shrub with trailing branches, bearing many oval, green *pads,* covered with clusters of spines; *flowers* solitary, large, at tips of pads, sepals many, greenish, petals many, yellow, many stamens in center; *fruits* oval, green, fleshy. *Distribution:* At low elevations on the northern islands, observed on Genovesa. ENDEMIC.

   Remarks: It is thought that the shrubby prickly pear grows on islands that never had large populations of tortoises. Another shrubby, endemic species can be seen on North Seymour.

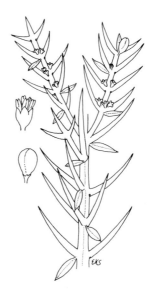

Scutia spicata (H. & B. ex Schult.) Weberb.
var. *pauciflora* (Hook.f.) M.C. Johnst.
Rhamnaceae   Espino, Thorn Shrub

Shrub with many stiff, green branches bearing long spines, often in opposite pairs; *leaves* usually alternate, small, elliptic or oblong, falling off easily; *flowers* very small, solitary or in clusters of 2–4 near bases of spines, calyx cup-shaped, petals 5, deeply lobed, yellowish; *fruits* oval, fleshy, green. *Distribution:* Common near shore and less frequent to middle elevations on most islands, sometimes forming thickets, noticeable at Punta Cormorante (Floreana), Academy Bay (Santa Cruz), South James Bay and Sullivan Bay (Santiago); also known in Ecuador.

Remarks: This is one of several shrubs that may be seen without leaves or flowers. It is the most spiny of these dry-zone plants, appearing as a dense tangle of smooth, green branches with obvious spines.

SHRUBS OF THE TRANSITION ZONE

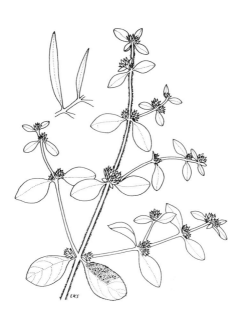

Alternanthera halimifolia (Lam.) Standl.
Amaranthaceae   Alternántera, Straw Flower

Shrub with branched stems, spreading or erect, often hairy; *leaves* opposite, elliptic to oval, covered with star-shaped hairs; *flowers* in dense clusters in axils of leaves, surrounded by dry bracts, sepals whitish, no petals; *fruits* usually not seen. *Distribution:* From low to higher elevations on several islands; common in *Scalesia* forest and near the New Road on Santa Cruz; also distributed in western South America.

   Remarks: There are several other species of *Alternanthera*, some endemic, which differ mainly in leaf shape. On Española and Santiago they have narrow leaves, but can be recognized by the distinctive, white, dry-textured flower clusters.

Caesalpinia bonduc (L.) Roxb.
Caesalpiniaceae   Mora

Shrub with curving branches, covered with hairs and scattered prickles; *leaves* alternate, compound, leaflets opposite, with pair of curved spines at the base, oval to oblong with pointed tip, slightly hairy; *inflorescences* erect near ends of branches; *flowers* with 5 sepals alternating with 5 separate, yellow petals, upper one sometimes curved, cluster of 10 stamens in center; *fruits* dry, oval to oblong, flat, covered with prickles. *Distribution:* At low elevations on two islands, forming a thicket near the Tortoise Reserve on Santa Cruz; also widely distributed in tropical areas.

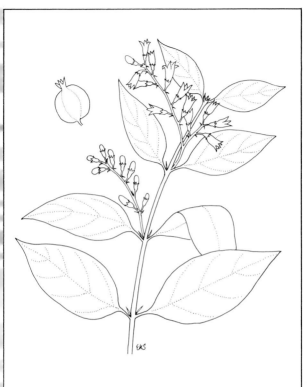

Chiococca alba (L.) Hitchc.
Rubiaceae   Espuela de Gallo, Milkberry

Shrub with spreading, slender branches; *leaves* opposite, narrowly to broadly oval with somewhat elongated tip, shiny dark green; *inflorescences* branched, in axils of leaves; *flowers* white, petals fused into a tube with 5 pointed lobes at top; *fruits* roundish, white, fleshy. *Distribution:* Dry to moist forests of several islands, at Black Beach (Floreana), and along trail at Tagus Cove (Isabela); also distributed in the American tropics.

SHRUBS OF TRANSITION ZONE

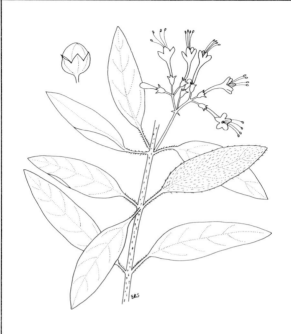

Clerodendrum molle HBK
Verbenaceae   Rodilla de caballo, Glorybower

Shrub with slender branches, bark grayish, marked with small spots; *leaves* opposite or in whorls of 3, elliptic, dark green, somewhat hairy; *inflorescences* much branched, in axils of leaves; *flowers* fragrant, calyx cup-shaped with 5 pointed lobes, petals white or pinkish, fused into long, slender tube, spreading into 5 lobes at top, stamens 4, protruding well beyond petals; *fruits* round, fleshy, separating into 4 parts. *Distribution:* Often in forests at middle elevations on the major islands, usually seen on trail to Salt Lake on Santiago, near Academy Bay and Tortoise Reserve (Santa Cruz), and at Tagus Cove (Isabela); also distributed from Central to South America.

Darwiniothamnus tenuifolius (Hook.f.) Harling
Asteraceae   Darwin's Aster

Shrub with many branches, slightly hairy; *leaves* alternate, narrow, aromatic, rarely hairy, clustered near tips of branches; *flower heads* sometimes solitary or arranged in compact inflorescences at ends of branches, rays white or purplish, narrow, disks yellow; *fruits* small, dry, ribbed, with bristles at top. *Distribution:* From sea level to moist forests on most islands, especially at Tagus Cove (Isabela) and along the New Road on Santa Cruz. ENDEMIC.

Ricinus communis L.
Euphorbiaceae   Higuerilla, Castor Bean

Shrub with smooth branches; *leaves* alternate, large, shiny green, palmately lobed, margins toothed; *inflorescences* spikes at ends of branches, with male flowers at base and female flowers near top; *flowers* small, greenish, sepals 5, pointed, no petals, with either a cluster of stamens or a round, spiny pistil in center; *fruits* dry, covered with coarse spines, containing bean-shaped, mottled seeds. *Distribution:* From low to middle elevations in open places on at least three islands, often observed along trails on Santa Cruz; also widely cultivated in warm regions, often escaping. INTRODUCED, POISONOUS.

   Remarks: The seeds of this plant are the source of castor oil, but are extremely poisonous if eaten.

Vallesia glabra (Cav.) Link
Apocynaceae   Peralillo, Pearl Berry

Shrub with slender branches; *leaves* alternate, narrowly elliptic to oblong, with pointed tip, surface smooth or sometimes
hairy underneath; *inflorescences* branched, in axils of leaves
or at ends of branches; *flowers* small, petals white, fused into
tube at bottom and separating into 5 lobes at top; *fruits* fleshy,
white, oval. *Distribution:* From sea level to higher elevations
in open areas or forests on the major islands, often seen at
Punta Cormorante (Floreana); hairy form ENDEMIC; smooth
form also distributed from Florida to South America.

Waltheria ovata Cav.
Sterculiaceae   Walteria, Velvet Shrub

Shrub with many slender branches, younger ones covered with star-shaped hairs; *leaves* alternate, light green, margins toothed, size variable, small, oval to very broad with heart-shaped bases, sometimes with 3 shallow lobes, surfaces covered with star-shaped hairs; *inflorescences* dense clusters in axils of leaves or at ends of branches; *flowers* small, petals 5, yellow, separate, narrowly oval; *fruits* dry, opening into 2 parts. *Distribution:* In dry areas from near shore to middle elevations on most islands, in extensive stands at Tagus Cove (Isabela), also at Punta Cormorante (Floreana) and on Genovesa; also known in Ecuador and Peru.

SHRUBS OF THE MICONIA
AND SCALESIA ZONES

Gossypium darwinii Watt.
Malvaceae   Algódon, Galápagos Cotton

Shrub with black-dotted stems, new growth often hairy;
leaves alternate, broad, usually 3-lobed, and covered with
black dots; *flowers* solitary in axils of leaves, large, calyx
5-parted and finely toothed on margins, petals 5, yellow with a
red-purple spot at base, a column of yellow stamens in center;
fruits dry, often 3-parted, opening to release seeds covered
with white hairs (cotton). *Distribution:* At higher elevations
on most islands, along trail at Tagus Cove (Isabela), and near
the New Road on Santa Cruz. ENDEMIC.

    Remarks: The other endemic species of cotton is not distrib-
uted so widely. It usually has unlobed leaves and less cotton on
the seeds.

Miconia robinsoniana Cogn.
Melastomataceae   Cacaotillo, Galápagos Miconia

Shrub, small branches 4-angled; *leaves* large, opposite, elliptic, with 3 parallel longitudinal veins joined by small, parallel
cross-veins; *inflorescences* much-branched, at ends of
branches; *flowers* small, magenta, with 5 separate petals and
curved stamens protruding; *fruits* oval, red. *Distribution:* At
higher elevations on Santiago, Santa Cruz, and San Cristóbal,
usually seen in dense stands above *Scalesia* forest on Santa
Cruz. ENDEMIC.

Remarks: This unique plant is perhaps the most endangered
in the Galápagos. On San Cristóbal and Santiago it has been
nearly destroyed by cattle grazing. The one remaining large
population on Santa Cruz has been damaged and needs continued protection.

variegated orange yellow + green leaves -

S. p. 40   found no where else in the world

Tournefortia psilostachya HBK
Boraginaceae   Southern Bittersweet

Shrub with slender, trailing, smooth branches, bark with brownish spots; *leaves* alternate, oval to elliptic, covered with fine hairs that give a satiny sheen; *inflorescences* near ends of branches, long, curved, and branched spikes bearing flowers along one side; *flowers* yellowish, petals fused into small tubes with 5 spreading lobes at top; *fruits* fleshy, round, orange. *Distribution:* Usually in shady places at all elevations on the major islands, obvious near the top of Santa Cruz along the New Road; also distributed in South America.

Remarks: From a distance, this plant with its bright orange berries resembles the bittersweet of North America. Two other endemic species of *Tournefortia* grow as upright shrubs, with the same branched and curved inflorescences, but with white fruits. One of these may be seen near Academy Bay (Santa Cruz).

VINES OF THE LITTORAL
AND DRY ZONES

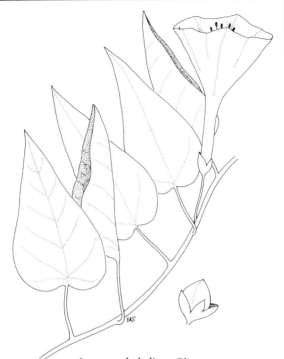

Ipomoea habeliana Oliv.
Convolvulaceae   Lava Morning Glory

Vine with thick stems creeping along the ground; *leaves* alternate, erect, broadly triangular, base rounded; *flowers* usually solitary in axils of leaves, on long stalks, petals white, fused into a tube that flares at top (funnel-shaped), usually open at night and early morning; *fruits* dry, oval with pointed tip, curved sepals persistent underneath. *Distribution:* Common on lava, often near cliffs, on several islands, usually seen on Genovesa. ENDEMIC.

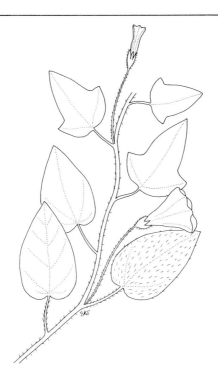

Ipomoea triloba L.
Convolvulaceae   Pink Morning Glory

Vine with slender stems, climbing over shrubs; *leaves* alternate, oval with heart-shaped base or divided into 3 lobes, surfaces somewhat hairy; *flowers* solitary in axils of leaves, on stalks, petals pink, fused into a small tube, flaring at top; *fruits* dry, round, hairy, separating into sections. *Distribution:* Common at low to middle elevations in open areas on the major islands, often seen along trail at South James Bay (Santiago); also distributed from southern United States to South America.

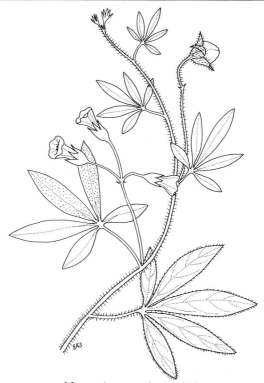

Merremia aegyptica (L.) Urban
Convolvulaceae   Hairy Morning Glory

Vine with slender, hairy stems; *leaves* alternate, divided into 5 fingerlike segments, each one elliptic with pointed tip, surfaces hairy, dotted with glands beneath; *flowers* solitary or clustered on long stalks in axils of leaves, sepals 5, very hairy, petals white, fused into tube with flaring top; *fruits* dry, round, opening into 4 segments, with persistent, hairy calyx beneath. *Distribution:* Common in dry wooded areas on most islands, often seen along trail at South James Bay (Santiago); also distributed from Mexico to South America.

Passiflora foetida L.
var. *galapagensis* Killip
Passifloraceae   Bedoca, Passion Flower

Vine with long trailing stems, covered with simple hairs; *leaves* alternate, 3-lobed, covered with gland-tipped hairs, long curling tendrils in axils; *flowers* single in axils of leaves, each one with finely divided, hairy green bracts below, sepals large, white and alternating with white petals, in center a ring of purple fringe, with stamens and the pistil standing up; *fruits* oval, fleshy, green to yellow, partially enclosed by the lacy bracts. *Distribution:* Climbing on rocks, shrubs, and trees from dry zone up to *Scalesia* forest, along trails and near Academy Bay (Santa Cruz). ENDEMIC.

Remarks: Two other species of passion flower occur in the islands. They differ in leaf shape, but have the same distinctive flowers.

VINES OF LITTORAL AND DRY ZONES

HERBS OF THE LITTORAL ZONE

Brachycereus nesioticus (K. Schum.) Backb.
Cactaceae   Cactillo de Lava, Lava Cactus

Herb with clumps of cylindrical, erect stems, brownish at base, yellowish at tips, covered with thick layer of spines; no *leaves; flowers* solitary, large, sepals many, narrow, reddish-brown, petals many, narrow, white, many stamens in center; *fruits* fleshy, oval, dark, with yellow spines. *Distribution:* On lava near coast of several islands, most obvious at Punta Espinosa (Fernandina). ENDEMIC.

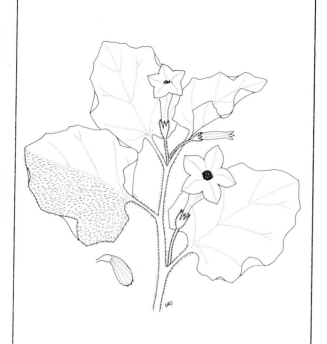

Cacabus miersii (Hook.f.) Wettst.
Solanaceae   Shore Petunia

Herb with trailing, hairy stems; *leaves* alternate but often close together and appearing opposite, shield-shaped with wavy or irregularly toothed margins, surfaces hairy; *flowers* in axils of leaves, petals white, united into a tube at base, expanding into 5 pointed lobes at top; *fruits* oval, fleshy, enclosed in ribbed calyx. *Distribution:* On beaches of several islands, seen on Genovesa and at Punta Espinosa (Fernandina), where it forms conspicuous ground cover; also known in Peru.

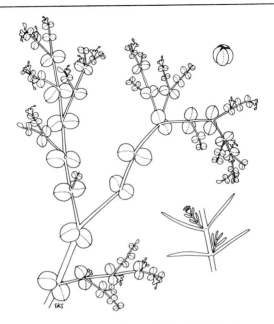

Chamaesyce amplexicaulis (Hook.f.) Burch
Euphorbiaceae   Spurge

Herb, woody at base, with low spreading branches, white sap in stems; *leaves* opposite, bright green, round, bases heart-shaped and wrapping around stems; *inflorescences* in axils of leaves, greenish, each one cup-shaped with tiny flowers inside; *male flowers* with stamens protruding, *female flowers* with round pistil protruding on a stalk; *fruits* dry, oval to round, breaking into sections. *Distribution:* Common on sand or lava near the shore of the major islands, especially obvious on Bartolomé and Genovesa. ENDEMIC.

Remarks: There are several other species in the islands, most of them endemic. They share the low, matlike habit and un-usual flowers, but differ in leaf shape. *C. viminea* (Hook.f.) Burch has very narrow leaves in clusters and can be seen on Genovesa and at Tagus Cove (Isabela).

Cyperus anderssonii Boeck.
Cyperaceae   Sedge

Herb, usually in clumps, stems triangular, erect; *leaves* alternate, erect, long and linear, tips pointed, base wrapped around stems; *inflorescences* in a whorl at top of stems, each branch bearing a spike of tiny flowers; *flowers* consisting of several overlapping bracts; *fruits* elliptical, dry, hard, small. *Distribution:* On sand or lava near the shores, less frequent in higher elevations, on major islands, most obvious on Bartolomé and bare lava field at Sullivan Bay (Santiago). ENDEMIC.

Remarks: This is one of many sedges in the Galápagos, some endemic and some of widespread distribution. They are very similar to grasses but usually can be distinguished by the triangular stems and the whorled or branched flowering spikes.

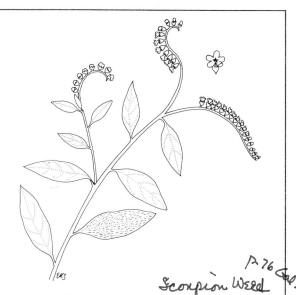

p. 76 Gal.

Scorpion Weed

Heliotropium angiospermum Murr.
Boraginaceae   Seaside Heliotrope

Herb, woody at base, low-growing and branched, stems
slightly hairy; *leaves* alternate, elliptic to oval, somewhat
hairy on back; *inflorescences* in axils of leaves, long, curved
spikes with flowers along one side, opening successively from
base toward tip; *flowers* small, petals white, fused at base, and
separated into 5 lobes at top; *fruits* round, dry, breaking into
several sections. *Distribution:* On sand or lava near the coasts
of nearly every island, at edge of white sand beach at Punta
Cormorante (Floreana) and among rocks on Genovesa; also
distributed in the New World tropics.

   Remarks: There are several other species of heliotrope in the
Galápagos that are very similar. They can be recognized as a
group by their distinctive inflorescence and low stature. *H.
curassavicum* has more succulent leaves and grows in salty
areas, such as Punta Suarez (Española). Heliotrope may be
seen also around the freshwater pools in the Tortoise Reserve
on Santa Cruz.

EKS

Polygala sancti-georgii Riley
Polygalaceae   Milkwort

Herb with slender, reddish, erect stems; *leaves* alternate, small, often crowded, oval to roundish or spoon-shaped; *inflorescences* short spikes at ends of stems; *flowers* small, sepals 5, 2 of them obvious and resembling petals, petals 3, enclosed by sepals, lavender to white, lower one boat-shaped with crest on top, upper 2 very small; *fruits* dry, oval, breaking into 2 parts. *Distribution:* In sandy or dry soil on a few islands, especially dunes near the white sand beach at Punta Cormorante (Floreana) and along trail at South James Bay (Santiago). ENDEMIC.

Remarks: There are two other endemic species that may be seen in similar habitats on Santiago and at Tagus Cove (Isabela). They differ in leaf shape but have the distinctive flowers.

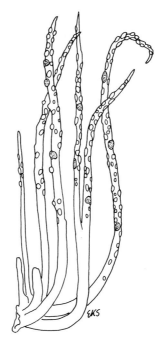

Roccella galapagoense Follmann
Roccellaceae   Orchil, Lichen

Herblike plant with upright or curved, tapering branches,
light gray, with irregular bumps on the surface; *no leaves,
flowers,* or *fruits. Distribution:* Growing on rocks near the
shore, very prominent on South Plaza. ENDEMIC.

Remarks: Orchil once was collected as a source of purple
dye. It is one of many species of lichens in the islands. These
unusual plants consist of a fungus that forms the body and
algal cells inside that manufacture food. Some lichens resemble a
crust of white, yellow, or orange on rocks or tree trunks.
Others are branched and green, growing upright or hanging
on branches of trees in several vegetation zones.

Sesuvium portulacastrum L.
Aizoaceae   Sea Purslane

Herb with trailing or erect, smooth stems, and alternate branches; *leaves* opposite, fleshy, fairly narrow to oblong, covered with tiny dots, turning red in dry season; *flowers* small, in axils of leaves on side branches, calyx pink, tubular with 5 broad, pointed lobes above, no petals; *seeds* small, black, and shiny. *Distribution:* Near the shore of several islands and forming extensive mats on South Plaza; also widely distributed in the tropics.

Remarks: This is the most colorful Galápagos plant when its foliage turns orange, then brilliant red. The endemic and widely distributed species *S. edmonstonei* is similar, but has white flowers. Both species look like *Portulaca*, but can be distinguished by the dots on the leaves, alternate branches, and the very different flowers.

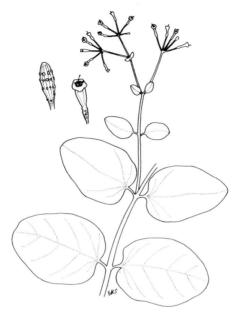

Commicarpus tuberosus (Lam.) Standl.
Nyctaginaceae   Wartclub

Herb with slender, trailing stems, much-branched; *leaves* opposite, oval to nearly round, base often heart-shaped; *inflorescences* rather elongated, branched, in axils of leaves; *flowers* small, petals reddish-purple, fused into tube with 5 shallow lobes at top; *fruits* dry, club-shaped, with 10 grooves and wartlike glands. *Distribution:* Widely distributed at lower elevations on most islands, common in undergrowth of cactus forest at Academy Bay (Santa Cruz); also known in Ecuador and Peru.

   Remarks: The closely related *Boerhaavia* is very similar in general appearance and flowers, but differs in having a triangular fruit with five lobes. It may be found in the same areas as wartclub.

Mollugo flavescens Anderss.
Molluginaceae   Molugo, Carpetweed

Herb with trailing or erect, delicate, branching stems, usually
tan-colored; *leaves* narrow to somewhat oval, smooth,
usually arranged in whorls; *flowers* in axils of leaves, small,
4–5 whitish sepals, no petals; *seeds* brown to black, shiny. *Distribution:* In dry zone of nearly all islands, especially obvious
as a colonizer of black lava flows at Sullivan Bay (Santiago).
ENDEMIC.

Remarks: This is the most widely distributed of several
species of carpetweed, all similar and all but one endemic.

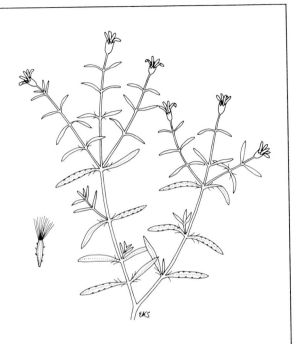

Pectis subsquarrosa (Hook.f.) Schultz-Bip.
Asteraceae   Pectis

Herb, much-branched to form a cushion-shape, stems shiny brown; *leaves* opposite, narrow, with glands near margins on underside and a few stiff hairs at base; *flower heads* at ends of branches, rays few, yellow, disks yellow; *fruits* small, dry, black, with bristles or scales at tip. *Distribution:* At low elevations on most islands, near top of trail at Tagus Cove (Isabela), and in sandy soil along trail at South James Bay (Santiago). ENDEMIC.

Remarks: This is a small but obvious plant, appearing from a distance as a mound of bright yellow flowers. Another species, not endemic, differs in having very narrow leaves.

Porophyllum ruderale (Jacq.) Cass.
var. *macrocephalum* (DC.) Cronq.
Asteraceae Poreleaf

Herb with branching, smooth stems; *leaves* alternate below and opposite on upper branches, oval with pointed tips, margins irregularly wavy, glands near margins; *flower heads* single at tips of leafy branches, rays narrow, purplish, just showing above narrow green bracts, disk not seen; *fruits* dry, with many stiff, whitish hairs attached, visible when bracts open. *Distribution:* On most islands, usually at lower elevations, along trail behind Espumillo Beach, and near the beach at South James Bay (Santiago); also a widely distributed weed in tropical America.

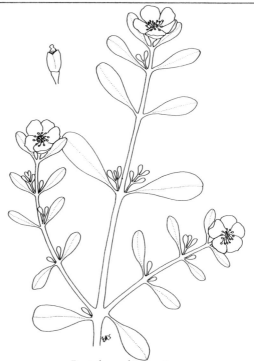

Portulaca oleracea L.
Portulacaceae   Verdolaga, Purslane

Herb with fleshy stems, trailing or erect; *leaves* opposite, oval to rounded, fleshy; *flowers* showy, in axils of leaves, petals 5, separate, yellow, many stamens in center; *fruits* dry, containing black seeds. *Distribution:* In dry zone of several islands, noticeable along trails on Santa Cruz, South Plaza and among rocks on North Seymour; also distributed nearly around the world.

   Remarks: Two other species of purslane occur in the Galápagos, one of them endemic. All three resemble *Sesuvium* in general appearance, but differ in having the obvious yellow flowers.

Sida salviifolia Presl.
Malvaceae   False Mallow

Herb with slender, hairy stems; *leaves* alternate, narrow, elliptic, margins often toothed, surfaces velvety, covered with star-
shaped hairs; *flowers* in axils of leaves, petals 5, white, with
cluster of yellow stamens protruding in center; *fruits* dry,
round, breaking into 5 segments. *Distribution:* In several
zones on most islands, along trails at Tagus Cove (Isabela) and
behind Espumillo Beach (Santiago); also distributed in the
New World tropics.

   Remarks: This is the most common of several similar species
of *Sida*, which vary in leaf shape. *S. hederifolia*, with oval
leaves, is found along the New Road on Santa Cruz.

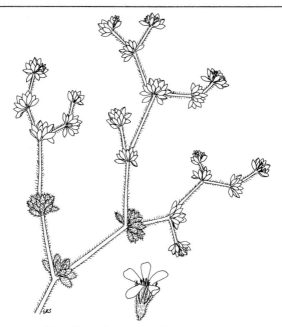

Tiquilia nesiotica (Howell) A. Richardson
Boraginaceae   Gray Matplant

Herb with woody base, branches hairy, spreading in round, matlike shape; *leaves* alternate, oval, small, crowded in clusters, surfaces covered with grayish hairs; *flowers* among leaves, very small and inconspicuous, petals white, fused into tube at base, separating into 5 oval lobes at top; *fruits* dry, hard, black. *Distribution:* On sand or ash slopes on Santiago and Bartolomé, where it is very common. ENDEMIC.

Remarks: The three other endemic species of *Tiquilia* are very similar and easily recognized by the low, round shape and grayish color. They are distributed more widely and may be seen at Tagus Cove (Isabela), South James Bay (Santiago), Punta Suarez (Española), and South Plaza. Their matlike shape allows them to take hold and grow as pioneer plants on shifting sands.

There another Hood (handwritten marginal note)

Trianthema portulacastrum L.
Aizoaceae   Horse Purslane

Herb with trailing or erect, smooth stems, red or with reddish splotches, opposite branches larger on one side; *leaves* opposite but of unequal sizes, oval to rounded, somewhat fleshy; *flowers* small, in axils of leaves on side branches, calyx tubular with 5 purplish lobes at top, no petals, numerous yellow stamens in center; *seeds* small, black, and wrinkled. *Distribution:* In dry zone on most islands, noticeable among rocks on trail at Punta Suarez (Española); also distributed in the tropics.

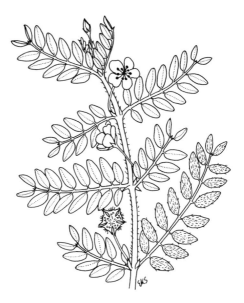

Tribulus cistoides L.
Zygophyllaceae   Cacho de Chivo, Punctureweed

Herb with woody base, hairy branches spreading on ground; *leaves* opposite, compound, one of each pair smaller, leaflets opposite, oval to elliptic, hairy; *flowers* on stalks, solitary in axils of leaves, petals 5, yellow, separate, oval, stamens 10 in center; *fruits* hard, green, hairy, in 5 segments, each with 2 prominent spines. *Distribution:* On dry soils near shore, on trail at South James Bay (Santiago), at Tagus Cove (Isabela) and Punta Suarez (Española); also widely distributed as a weed in warmer regions, especially Mexico and the Caribbean.

Remarks: Another very similar species of punctureweed is less common. Although the flowers of *Tribulus* resemble *Portulaca*, they differ in having only 10 stamens. The combination of compound leaves and spiny fruits makes this plant distinctive.

HERBS OF THE
TRANSITION ZONE

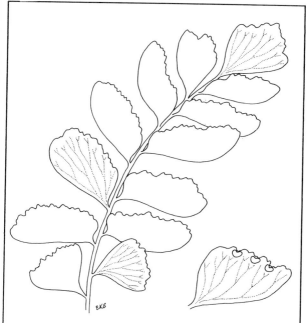

Adiantum concinnum Willd.
Polypodiaceae   Maidenhair Fern

Herb with creeping stems; *fronds* delicate, curving, compound, stalk shiny brown, segments alternate, oval to fan-shaped, upper margin lobed; *no flowers; fruiting bodies* crescent-shaped, along margins of segments on underside. *Distribution:* In rocky areas from low to higher elevations on major islands, often seen along trail through woods behind Espumillo Beach (Santiago); also distributed in the West Indies, Mexico, and South America.

Remarks: There are four other species of maidenhair fern in the islands, all similar in appearance and usually growing in moist places.

The endemic shrub *Miconia* is one of the few Galápagos plants to have reddish flowers.

The unusual daisy tree, *Scalesia*, has rather inconspicuous white flower heads and leaves in clusters near the tips of branches.

The balsa tree is an example of an introduced plant that has spread into the native forest.

Ricinus (castor bean) is a poisonous plant that has been introduced and allowed to spread.

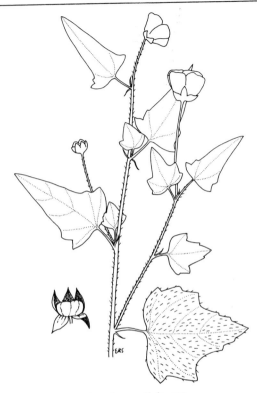

Anoda acerifolia DC.
Malvaceae   Anoda

Herb with branching, hairy stems; *leaves* alternate, triangular
to 3-lobed and coarsely toothed, with scattered hairs; *flowers*
single in axils of leaves, on long stalks, petals 5, white, separate, with a cluster of yellow stamens in center; *fruits* round,
dry, made up of several segments that break open, with persistent sepals underneath. *Distribution:* At higher elevations
along the New Road on Santa Cruz; widely distributed in the
New World tropics.

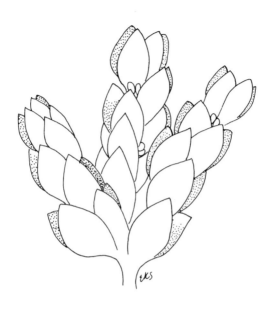

Azolla microphylla Kaulf.
Azollaceae   Water Fern

Herb, floating on surface of water, branches alternate; *fronds 2-lobed,* wrapping around stems and overlapping, green turning red for part of the year; *no flowers; fruiting bodies* small, round, in pairs among leaves, releasing 2 kinds of spores. *Distribution:* Floating on freshwater pools, often forming a nearly solid mat, on the major islands, likely to be seen near Tortoise Reserve on Santa Cruz; also distributed in the West Indies, Central America, and South America.

Remarks: Studies of fossil spores have shown that another species of *Azolla* lived in the islands thousands of years ago. Apparently, it died off when the ponds dried up for a long period and was replaced about 10,000 years ago by this species.

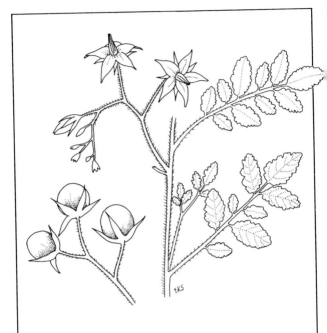

Lycopersicon cheesmanii Riley
Solanaceae   Tomatillo, Galápagos Tomato

Herb, low-growing, much-branched, hairy; *leaves* alternate, compound, segments irregularly lobed; *inflorescences* branched; *flowers* with 5 yellow, pointed petals, curved backward, anthers fused into a tube in center; *fruits* fleshy, small, round, yellow to orange, with 5 narrow calyx segments persistent beneath. *Distribution:* From low to middle elevations on most islands, often seen at top of trail at Tagus Cove (Isabela). ENDEMIC.

Remarks: The seeds of this plant have very thick coats and seem to germinate best after they have passed through the intestine of a tortoise or bird. Recently, this salt-tolerant species has been used to breed hybrid tomatoes that can be cultivated in salty soil.

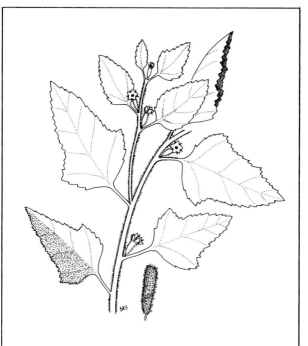

Mentzelia aspera L.
Loasaceae   Stickleaf

Herb with stems covered with barbed and pointed hairs; *leaves* alternate, oval to 3-lobed, margins toothed, surfaces hairy; *flowers* solitary in axils of leaves, sepals hairy, petals 5, yellow, with cluster of stamens in center; *fruits* dry, cylindrical, hairy. *Distribution:* Common at low elevations on most islands, often seen in *Bursera* woods behind Espumillo Beach (Santiago); also distributed from Mexico to South America.

  Remarks: The barbed hairs on the fruits help them to stick to birds, animals, or humans and get distributed to new areas. Visitors should remove fruits from shoes, socks, and pants legs before going on to another island.

Pennisetum purpureum Schum.
Poaceae   Pasta Elefante, Elephant Grass

Herb with tall (shrub height), round, straight stems, often in clumps; *leaves* alternate, erect or curving, long and linear, tips pointed, bases wrapped around stems; *inflorescences* stiff, brushlike spikes, bearing tiny flowers surrounded by long bristles, yellowish or purple; *fruits* small, dry, hard. *Distribution:* At mid-elevations on Santa Cruz; also widely distributed in the tropics. INTRODUCED.

Remarks: This native of Africa was introduced to the Galápagos fairly recently and has spread rapidly in disturbed areas. It serves as an example of the many species of grasses (native and endemic) in the islands. They all have similar growth form and leaves, but are only 2 to 3 feet tall. The inflorescences vary from simple to compound, with or without bristles. During the dry season, grasses will be a golden-tan color. Several species may be observed at low elevations, especially on Santa Cruz, Santiago (including the fresh lava flow at Sullivan Bay), Genovesa, and North Seymour.

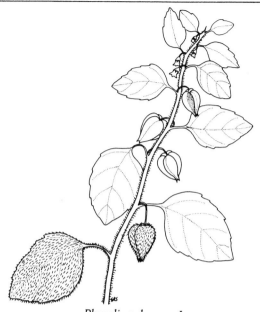

Physalis pubescens L.
Solanaceae   Uvilla, Ground Cherry

Herb with hairy branches; *leaves* alternate, oval, bases unequal, margins irregularly toothed, surfaces hairy; *flowers* solitary in axils of leaves, on drooping stalks, sepals fused below, divided into 5 pointed lobes above, petals yellow with dark spot at base, fused into tube with 5 shallow lobes at top; *fruits* fleshy, enclosed in inflated, hairy calyx with 5 ridges. *Distribution:* In open or shady places from low to middle elevations on several islands, usually seen along the New Road and near Academy Bay on Santa Cruz; also distributed from the United States to South America.

Remarks: The endemic species *P. galapagoensis* is very similar and may be found in the same areas, although it is more common at lower elevations. It differs in lacking the dark spot on the petals and hairs on the inflated calyx. Both plants resemble the cultivated Japanese lantern.

Salvia occidentalis Sw.
Lamiaceae Salvia

Herb with erect, square, hairy, branched stems; *leaves* opposite, oval to diamond-shaped, hairy, margins toothed; *inflorescences* long spikes in axils of leaves and at ends of branches; *flowers* small, arranged in whorls around stem, calyx covered with glandular hairs, petals blue or lavender, fused into a tube below and separating into 2 parts above, upper lip erect, lower lip with 3 unequal lobes; *fruits* dry, hard, brown, elliptic. *Distribution:* In moist, shady places on the major islands, often seen in woods behind Espumillo Beach (Santiago); also distributed from Florida to South America.

Remarks: There are three other species of salvia in the islands, all endemic and very limited in distribution. They are similar, with blue to pale lavender or nearly white flowers.

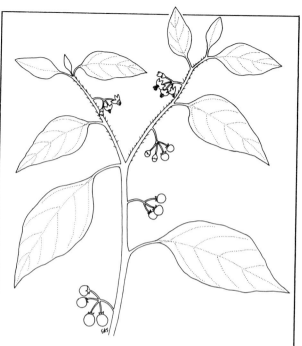

Solanum americanum Mill.
Solanaceae   Nightshade

Herb with trailing stems, younger ones hairy; *leaves* alternate, oval to diamond-shaped, margins unevenly toothed, surfaces sometimes hairy; *inflorescences* whorls of flowers at ends of drooping stalks, on stem between leaves; *flowers* white, petals 5, pointed and curved backward, stamens fused into a tube protruding in center; *fruits* fleshy, round, purple to black. *Distribution:* From low to middle elevations along trails or in woods, often seen near the New Road on Santa Cruz; also distributed as a weed in the New World.

Remarks: There are two other species of *Solanum* that are similar, but grow into shrubs with yellow to orange fruits. One of them can be seen on Santa Cruz, from low elevations up to the *Scalesia* forest.

HERBS OF TRANSITION ZONE

Verbena litoralis HBK
Verbenaceae   Verbena, Vervain

Herb, sometimes woody at base, with erect, squarish, hairy stems; *leaves* opposite, narrow to oblong, margins toothed along upper half, surfaces hairy; *inflorescences* long spikes in axils of leaves or at ends of branches, flowering from base upward; *flowers* small, petals blue, lavender or pink, fused into a tube at base and spreading into 5 lobes at top; *fruits* dry, hard, opening into 4 sections. *Distribution:* From low to higher elevations on several islands, often seen along the New Road on Santa Cruz; also widely distributed as a weed from southern United States to South America.

Remarks: There are four other endemic species of verbena that are similar in general appearance, differing in leaf shape or in having white flowers. Some of these may be seen at Tagus Cove (Isabela), Academy Bay (Santa Cruz), or South James Bay (Santiago).

HERBS OF THE MICONIA AND SCALESIA ZONES

Bidens pilosa L.
Asteraceae   Beggar's Ticks.

Herb with branched stems, somewhat hairy; *leaves* opposite, oval to diamond-shaped, varying from simple to 3-parted to compound, margins toothed, surfaces slightly hairy; *flower heads* single on long stalks at ends of branches, rays yellowish-white with fine lines, sometimes absent, disk yellow; *fruits* dry, long and narrow, with barbed projections at tips. *Distribution:* Known from several islands, likely to be seen near top of Santa Cruz along the New Road; also widely distributed in tropics and subtropics.

Remarks: The fruits stick readily to animals and humans who then carry them to new areas. Two other very similar species of *Bidens* occur in the islands.

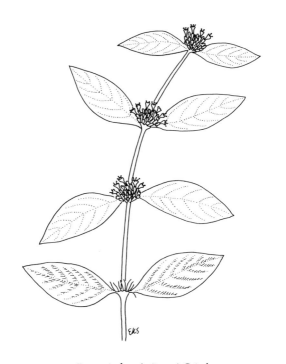

Borreria laevis (Lam.) Griseb.
Rubiaceae   Buttonherb

Herb with erect or trailing stems, usually smooth; *leaves*
opposite, oval with pointed tips, surface hairy along veins, a
sheath bearing filaments on its edge just below the leaves;
flowers small, in dense clusters on stem in axils of leaves,
petals white, fused into a tube with 4 lobes at top and tiny
stamens often protruding; *fruits* dry, small, in tight clusters.
Distribution: Along trails or in clearings at higher elevations
on several islands, seen along the New Road on Santa Cruz;
also a weed of disturbed areas in tropical America.

Capsicum galapagense Heiser & Smith
Solanaceae   Aji de Monte, Galápagos Pepper

Herb, much-branched and shrubby, with hairy stems; *leaves* alternate, elliptic to oval; *flowers* solitary in axils of leaves, petals white, fused into short tube below, separating into 5 pointed lobes at top, stamens fused into tube in center; *fruits* fleshy, roundish, red-orange. *Distribution:* Moist, shady woods on Santa Cruz and Isabela, often seen along the New Road on Santa Cruz. ENDEMIC.

Remarks: There are two other species of pepper, one endemic, that differ in having oblong, darker red fruits. All resemble the ornamental peppers grown as houseplants.

HERBS OF MICONIA AND SCALESIA ZONES

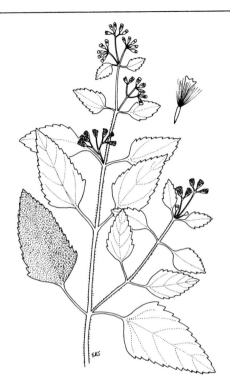

Eupatorium pycnocephalum Less.
Asteraceae   Boneset

Herb, erect or trailing over other plants, stems hairy; *leaves* opposite, oval to triangular, hairy, margins toothed; *inflorescences* branched, in axils of leaves and at ends of branches; *flower heads* surrounded by ribbed bracts, no rays, disk flowers blue, pink, or white, small, tubular; *fruits* dry, wedge-shaped, black, with clusters of bristles at tips. *Distribution:* At higher elevations along the New Road on Santa Cruz, likely to spread; also distributed as a weed from southwestern United States to South America.

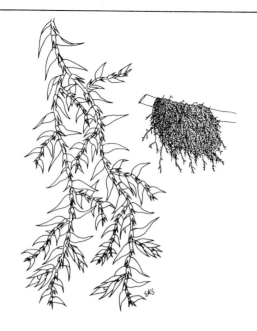

Frullania aculeata Tayl.
Frullaniaceae   Liverwort

Herb with many, slender, brown, alternate branches, hanging in dense clumps on trees; *leaves* brown, 2-lobed, larger lobe triangular with elongated, pointed tip, smaller lobe with 2 pointed teeth; *no flowers*, but male and female reproductive structures on short branches; *fruiting bodies* small, opening to release tiny spores. *Distribution:* Common on trees in the wet forests on several islands, best seen on *Scalesia* along the New Road on Santa Cruz.

Remarks: Frullania is a representative of the many liverworts and mosses (known collectively as bryophytes) in the Galápagos, usually at higher elevations. This brown plant is visible in trees from a distance and was the basis for early descriptions of a "Brown Zone" in the vegetation. This area now is included in the *Scalesia* Zone.

Justicia galapagana Lindau
Acanthaceae   Justicia

Herb with many erect, hairy branches; *leaves* opposite, oval to lance-shaped, hairy; *inflorescences* branched, in axils of leaves or at ends of branches; *flowers* alternate, petals purple, fused into a tube below, separating into 2 parts at top, the lower lip with 3 lobes, stamens 2, just protruding from tube; *fruits* dry, club-shaped, hairy. *Distribution:* In moist forests on several islands, often seen along the New Road on Santa Cruz. ENDEMIC.

Lycopodium clavatum L.
Lycopodiaceae   Licopodio, Clubmoss

Herb with creeping stems and erect branches, these with secondary branches like candelabra; *leaves* small, spirally
arranged around stems, narrow with pointed tip; conelike
structures at ends of branches bear *fruiting bodies,* each one
small, round, covered by a yellowish scale and releasing
powdery masses of yellow spores. *Distribution:* In shady,
usually moist places on several islands, likely to be seen in
Scalesia forest or under *Miconia* shrubs near the New Road on
Santa Cruz; also widely distributed from Canada to South
America.

Remarks: There are five other species of clubmoss in the
islands, all of which also grow in warmer regions of the New
World. Two of these also live on the ground and resemble *L.
clavatum.* The others usually grow on branches of trees in the
moist forest.

Plumbago scandens L.
Plumbaginaceae   Leadwort

Herb with slender, trailing stems, often reddish; *leaves* alternate, elliptic to oval; *inflorescences* long spikes at ends of branches; *flowers* white to pinkish, calyx covered with glands, petals united in narrow tube spreading into 5 rounded lobes at top; *fruits* oval, dry, thin-walled. *Distribution:* In forests up to higher elevations on several islands, often seen along the New Road on Santa Cruz; also distributed in the New World tropics.

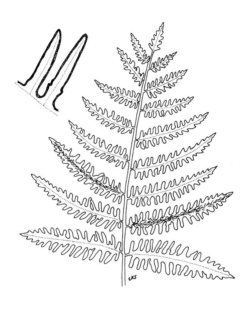

Pteridium aquilinum (L.) Kuhn
var. *arachnoideum* (Kaulf.) Herter
Polypodiaceae   Bracken Fern

Herb with large, curving fronds; *fronds* compound, triangular, sometimes hairy underneath, segments alternate, elliptic with pointed tips, margins deeply lobed; *no flowers; fruiting bodies* along margins of segments on underside in continuous bands. *Distribution:* In open areas or under trees and shrubs, mostly at higher elevations on several islands, frequently seen under *Miconia* near the New Road on Santa Cruz; also distributed in Mexico, the West Indies, and South America.

   Remarks: Bracken fern grows nearly everywhere in the temperate and warm zones. In some areas it has evolved into recognizable varieties, like this one.

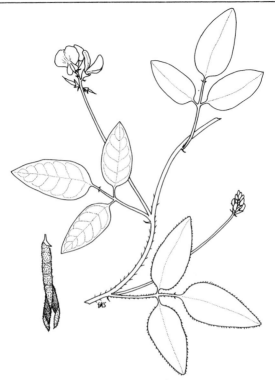

Vigna luteola (Jacq.) Benth.
Fabaceae   Wild Cowpea

Herb with trailing stems, sometimes hairy; *leaves* alternate, on long stalks, compound with 3 leaflets, usually oval, but varying to narrow, sometimes hairy; *inflorescences* with a few flowers on long, erect stalks in axils of leaves; *flowers* yellow, petals 5, upper one large and erect, lower 2 boat-shaped, with 2 wings at sides; *fruits* dry, elongated, sometimes hairy. *Distribution:* At higher elevations on Santa Cruz, Isabela, and Fernandina, usually seen along the New Road on Santa Cruz; also widely distributed in tropical areas.

CULTIVATED PLANTS

The Galápagos climate is favorable to both tropical and temperate plants. Residents have brought to the islands many ornamentals and crops, especially those grown in Ecuador. Most of these have remained in gardens, but some crops have invaded the native vegetation. The list below includes some of the more common plants that may be observed near settlements on Floreana and Santa Cruz, but other plants are also in cultivation. For convenience, they are divided into three categories.

Tropical and Subtropical Ornamentals

Bougainvillea glabra (bougainvillea). Vine with oval leaves; flowers in clusters, each surrounded by showy pink, orange, red, or purplish bracts.

Datura arborea (floripondo, tree datura). Tree with spreading branches; leaves alternate, oval; flowers very large, yellowish, funnel-shaped, and hanging down from branches.

Delonix regia (poinciana). Tree or shrub with compound leaves; flowers orange-red, with 5 separate, ruffled petals; fruits dry and elongated.

Hibiscus tiliaceus (hibiscus). Shrub with oval to heart-shaped, hairy leaves; flowers saucer-shaped with column of stamens in center, petals yellow at first, then turning orange to red. *Remarks:* This shrub and other species of hibiscus with large, red flowers have escaped cultivation in some places.

Nerium oleander (oleander). Shrub with narrow, shiny leaves; flowers in clusters, petals pink or white, fused into a tube with 5 lobes at top. *Remarks:* Although a popular ornamental, oleander is poisonous.

Terminalia catappa (almendro, tropical almond). Tree with branches in whorls; leaves large, spoon-shaped; fruits greenish, almond-shaped, in clusters. *Remarks:* The fruits of this tree are edible, but it has not been cultivated extensively in the Galápagos.

Tropical or Subtropical Crops

Carica papaya (papaya). Tree with straight trunk; crown of
large, palmately lobed leaves at top; fruits large, roundish,
yellow-green.

Citrus species (lemon, orange, lime). Tree with thorns; leaves
alternate, leathery, oval; flowers white, very fragrant;
fruits oval to round with leathery skin, yellow, green, or
orange.

Cocos nucifera (coco, coconut palm). Tree with tall, straight,
or curved trunk; whorl of large, compound leaves at the
top; fruits in clusters, round, hard, and brown. *Remarks:*
Although widely distributed on tropical beaches, coconut
palm apparently has not been able to grow outside cultivation in the Galápagos.

Coffea arabica (café, coffee). Shrub with shiny, opposite
leaves; flowers white, fragrant; fruits in clusters, fleshy,
red to black (the seeds inside are the coffee "beans").
Remarks: Galápagos coffee once was exported to the
mainland.

Musa species (plátano, banana). Small tree with straight trunk;
leaves very long and fairly narrow, edges usually split;
fruits in long, branched clusters hanging down under
leaves, fleshy, with leathery skins, green turning yellow.

Persea americana (aguacate, avocado). Tall tree with alternate,
large, elliptic leaves; fruits green, pear-shaped.

Saccharum officinarum (caña de azúcar, sugar cane). Herb,
grasslike, tall, with thick jointed stems containing sweet
juice; leaves long and narrow.

Houseplants

Familiar house and/or garden plants such as *Rosa* (rose) and
Pelargonium (geranium), as well as those listed below, may be
seen in outdoor gardens in the Galápagos.

Codiaeum species (croton). Shrub with large, leathery leaves,
dark green, with variegated patterns of yellow, orange,
and red.

Cyperus alternifolius (umbrella sedge). Herb with tall stem;
leaves in a whorl at the top, narrow, resembling spokes of
an umbrella.

Euphorbia lactea (milkstripe euphorbia). Shrub, cactuslike, with candelabra branches, green with irregular white stripe in center, single spines along edge; leaves small or absent.

Euphorbia tirucalli (pencil euphorbia). Shrub with alternate, fleshy, green branches that divide again into pairs of narrow branches; leaves absent. *Remarks:* Like all euphorbias, these two species contain a milky sap that is irritating to the skin.

Ficus species (higo, fig). Tree with leathery, shiny green leaves, oval to fiddle-shaped; fruits small and green.

Sansevieria species (snake plant). Herb with no stem; leaves tall, narrow, erect, fleshy, green with markings or borders of yellowish-white.

GLOSSARY

Aerial: Growing in the air.

Alternate: Placed singly one above the other on alternate sides of the stem.

Axil: An angle formed between the leaf and the stem.

Barb: A stiff hair with a hooked tip.

Bark: The outer covering on the stem (trunk) of a woody plant.

Bract: A modified, reduced leaf.

Branch: A secondary stem arising from the main stem (trunk).

Bristle: A stiff hair.

Calyx: The outer series of flower parts, composed of sepals, usually green.

Compound: Composed of two or more similar parts.

Cone: A cluster of scales arranged around a central stem and bearing reproductive structures.

Crest: An elevated ridge on the surface.

Disk: Central portion of flower head in daisy family (Asteraceae); composed of tiny, tubular flowers.

Endemic: A plant that grows only in the Galápagos Islands.

Entire: Margin of a leaf (or petal) that has no teeth.

Filament: A threadlike structure.

Flower: The reproductive part of a higher plant, made up of modified leaves: sepals and/or petals, stamens bearing pollen to bring about fertilization, and/or a pistil containing ovules that will mature into seeds.

Frond: The leaf of a fern.

Fruit: The ripened ovary of a flowering plant, containing seeds.

Fruiting body: A structure bearing spores (on a nonflowering plant).

Germinate: To begin to grow.

Gland: A secretory structure.

Head: A short, dense cluster of small flowers.

Herb: A plant lacking persistent woody parts above ground, although sometimes bases of stems are woody; used here to include nonflowering plants.

Inflorescence: The flowering portion of a plant.

Introduced: A plant purposely brought to the Galápagos by humans.

Leaf: A flat outgrowth of a stem, usually green and capable of manufacturing food.

Leaflet: One part of a compound leaf.

Lobe: A partial, rounded division of a plant part.

Opposite: Arranged in pairs on opposite sides of the stem.

Pad: The flattened branch of a cactus plant.

Palmate: Divided in a handlike manner.

Persistent: Remaining attached.

Petal: One part of the corolla or inner series of modified leaves surrounding a flower, usually colored.

Pistil: The central, seed-bearing part of a flower, consisting of the basal ovary, the narrow style, and the sticky stigma, which receives pollen.

Prickle: A small, sharp outgrowth on the surface.

Prop root: A root above ground that helps support the plant.

Ray: Outer, small, strap-shaped flower of the flower head in daisy family (Asteraceae).

Rib: A prominent nerve or vein.

Rootstock: Underground stem.

Scale: A thin, dry leaf or bract.

Sepal: One part of the calyx or outer series of modified leaves surrounding a flower, usually green.

Sheath: A tubular structure completely or partially surrounding a stem.

Shrub: A persistent, woody plant with several stems from the base.

Spike: An elongated inflorescence with small flowers.

Spine: A sharp, rigid outgrowth from a stem.

Spore: A reproductive cell of nonflowering plants (comparable to a seed).

Stalk: The stem of any organ of a plant.

Stamen: The pollen-bearing part of a flower, consisting of the narrow filament supporting the usually yellow anther, which bears pollen.

Stem: The main axis of a plant, supporting leaves and flowers.
Toothed: With small indentations along the margin.
Tree: A persistent woody plant with one trunk from the base.
Trunk: The main stem of a tree.
Vine: A plant with long, flexible stems, trailing on the ground or climbing on other plants, never growing upright.
Whorl: Arranged in a circle.
Winged: Having a thin, membranous extension.

ISLAND CHECKLISTS

Bartolomé

- *Chamaesyce**
- *Conocarpus*
- *Cryptocarpus*
- *Cyperus*
- *Maytenus*
- *Opuntia* (tree)
- Poaceae
- *Rhizophora*
- *Scutia*
- *Sesuvium*
- *Tiquilia**
- *Waltheria*

Española

Gardner Bay
- *Acacia*
- *Cryptocarpus*
- *Opuntia* (tree)
- Poaceae
- *Tiquilia*

Punta Suarez
- *Alternanthera*
- *Atriplex**
- *Cryptocarpus*
- *Grabowskia**
- ∨ *Heliotropium*
- *Lycium**
- *Tiquilia*
- *Trianthema**
- *Tribulus*

Genovesa

- *Bursera*
- *Cacabus*
- *Chamaesyce*
- *Cordia* (shrub)*
- *Croton*
- *Cryptocarpus*
- Cyperaceae
- *Heliotropium*
- *Ipomoea habeliana**
- *Lantana*
- *Opuntia* (shrub)*
- Poaceae
- *Waltheria*

Fernandina

Punta Espinosa
- *Brachycereus**
- *Cacabus**
- *Laguncularia**
- *Maytenus*
- *Rhizophora**

Floreana

Black Beach
- *Acacia*
- *Chiococca*

Post Office Bay
- *Cryptocarpus*
- *Parkinsonia*

*Most prominent or significant plants.

Punta Cormorante
Avicennia
Bursera
Castela
Cryptocarpus
Heliotropium
Jasminocereus
Lantana
*Lecocarpus**
Maytenus
~*Nolana**
*Parkinsonia**
*Polygala**
Prosopis
*Scaevola**
Scalesia (shrub)*
Scutia
*Vallesia**
Waltheria

Isabela
Tagus Cove
Bursera
Chamaesyce
Chiococca
Clerodendrum
Cordia (tree)
Croton
*Darwiniothamnus**
*Gossypium**
Lantana
*Lycopersicon**
*Macraea**

Opuntia
*Pectis**
Polygala
Scalesia (shrub)
Sida
Tiquilia
Tribulus
Verbena
*Waltheria**

North Seymour
*Bursera malocophylla**
Opuntia (shrub)*
Poaceae
Portulaca

Rabida
Avicennia
Bursera
Conocarpus
*Cryptocarpus**
Maytenus

Santa Cruz
Academy Bay
*Acacia**
Castela
Clerodendrum
Commicarpus
Cordia (tree)*
Cryptocarpus
*Hippomane**
*Jasminocereus**

Opuntia (tree)*
Parkinsonia
Passiflora
Physalis
Portulaca
Rhizophora
Scutia
Tournefortia
Verbena

New Road to Highlands
Alternanthera
Anoda
Bambusa
Bidens
Borreria
Capsicum
Cinchona
Cyathea*
Darwiniothamnus*
Eupatorium
Frullania*
Gossypium
Justicia
Lycopodium*
Miconia*
Ochroma
Passiflora
Pennisetum
Physalis
Plumbago
Psidium*
Pteridium*
Ricinus
Scalesia (tree)*

Solanum
Tournefortia
Verbena
Vigna
Zanthoxylum*

Tortoise Reserve
Azolla*
Caesalpinia*
Clerodendrum
Heliotropium

Santiago

Espumillo Beach
Acacia
Adiantum*
Avicennia*
Bursera
Cassia*
Castela
Conocarpus*
Hippomane
Laguncularia
Mentzelia
Porophyllum
Salvia
Sida

Salt Lake
Batis*
Bursera
Cassia
Castela
Clerodendrum
Cordia (tree)*

Poaceae
Scutia
South James Bay
Acacia *
Alternanthera
Bursera *
Cassia
Castela
Croton *
Ipomoea triloba *
Merremia *
Opuntia (tree)
Pectis
Poaceae
Polygala
Porophyllum
Scutia
Tiquilia
Tribulus

Sullivan Bay
Batis *
Bursera
Cyperus *
Maytenus
Mollugo *
Poaceae
Scutia

South Plaza
Castela
Grabowskia
Maytenus *
Opuntia (tree) *
Portulaca
Roccella *
Sesuvium *
Tiquilia

Dotted lines indicate trails. Open circles indicate craters. Black areas indicate salt lagoons and lakes. Shaded areas indicate cliffs along the uplifted side of the islands.

PUNTA
ESPINOSA

FERNANDINA

Dotted lines indicate trails. *Open circles* indicate craters. *Black areas* indicate salt lagoons and lakes.

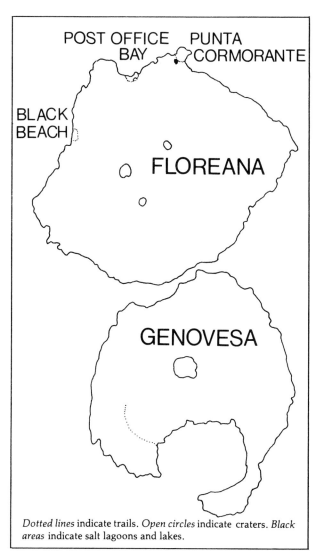

POST OFFICE BAY   PUNTA CORMORANTE

BLACK BEACH

FLOREANA

GENOVESA

Dotted lines indicate trails. *Open circles* indicate craters. *Black areas* indicate salt lagoons and lakes.

TAGUS
COVE

ISABELA

Dotted lines indicate trails. *Open circles* indicate craters. *Black areas* indicate salt lagoons and lakes.

Dotted lines indicate trails. *Open circles* indicate craters. *Black areas* indicate salt lagoons and lakes.

Dotted lines indicate trails. *Open circles* indicate craters. *Black areas* indicate salt lagoons and lakes.

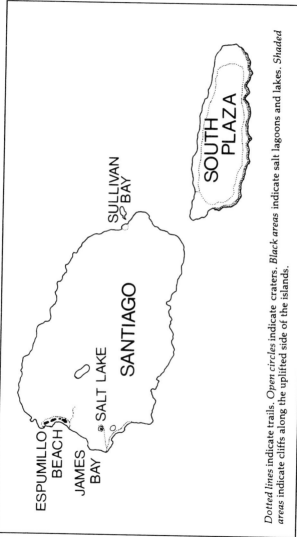

Dotted lines indicate trails. *Open circles* indicate craters. *Black areas* indicate salt lagoons and lakes. *Shaded areas* indicate cliffs along the uplifted side of the islands.

HELPFUL HINTS

You will receive additional useful information from your tour agent, but here are a few hints, based on personal experience, to make your trip more enjoyable.

Clothing

1. Take casual, comfortable clothes, including long pants and one shirt with long sleeves to prevent overexposure to sun.
2. Essential items are a hat and sunglasses to shade you from the hot equatorial sun that is directly overhead most of the day.
3. You will need sturdy sneakers or hiking shoes with nonslip soles and preferably with high tops to prevent turning your ankles on rough lava.
4. If you enjoy swimming, take a bathing suit, for there will be several opportunities to swim and snorkel in the warmish waters.
5. For cool evenings at sea, take a sweater or light jacket.

Health

1. As on all trips, take an adequate supply of prescription drugs or any health items not available in foreign countries.
2. If you sail to or from the islands, you may encounter rough seas. Prepare yourself by taking motion-sickness medication, starting one or two days before you sail. The waters around the islands usually are calm.
3. Suntan lotion is essential for everyone, and if you are very sensitive to sun, take a sunblock for lips and nose and a sunburn remedy.
4. Insect repellent is not really necessary, although there may be a few mosquitoes around the town on Santa Cruz (and in Guayaquil).

Photography

1. Take whatever camera equipment you have, for the photographic possibilities in the islands are endless. Although

you can get very close to most birds, animals, and plants, a telephoto lens is useful. Don't take a new camera or a lens that you don't know how to use!

2. Take more film than you think you will need. The price of film in Ecuador is exorbitant.

3. Because the sunlight is so bright, you don't need very fast film. The photographs in this book were taken at ASA 64.

4. Professional photographers warn that airport X-rays can damage film. Hand-carry your camera through security and protect your film with a lead-lined bag.

Notes on Ecuador

1. Your itinerary should include a few days in Ecuador, a country with friendly people, interesting crafts, and spectacular scenery.

2. The native flora of Ecuador is too large and varied to understand in a short visit, but you will recognize many cultivated plants. The cool climate in Quito allows flowers to bloom all year round.

3. Your summer-weight clothes will do in humid Guayaquil, but Quito is likely to be quite cool at night. Either take a warm jacket or buy one of the local, handwoven ponchos.

4. Although the water in Ecuador is reported to be pure, visitors do pick up intestinal parasites or bacterial infections. To be safe, drink bottled sparkling water.

JOURNAL

JOURNAL

INDEX

Latin plant names and page numbers for color plates are in italics.

Punthieva maculata -
       brown-spotted orchids. 41 Stedman
one of 11 species of orchid

                    Red Round leaves
                        white flowers
Three   ] Hood
Scorpion Tail
      ~ blue leaves

ACKNOWLEDGMENTS

I greatly appreciate the loan of Galápagos plant specimens from the herbarium of the New York Botanical Garden. Special thanks are given to my husband, Ted Barkley, for his critical reading of the manuscript and helpful suggestions. Thanks also to Ellen and George Henke and Duncan Porter for their comments.

This is Contribution No. 364 from the Charles Darwin Foundation for the Galápagos Islands.